# Preface

The thought first struck me as I hovered back and forth between C. S. Lewis and Rick Warren. The lobby, which housed the bookstore, was enormous. I smelled the beans brewing at the adjacent coffee shop. The church was apparently successful enough to house its own version of Starbucks *and* Barnes and Noble.

The conference I was attending had the familiar trappings: welcome bags, break-out sessions, hesitantly exchanged business cards. There were key note speakers, shared ideas about innovation, and stale turkey sandwiches consumed while swapping trade secrets. It was all fairly normal…until the overzealous guy from Tulsa asked me, unsolicited, if he could "pray for my sins". That encounter preceded a session where I squirmed in my chair as two Christian women awkwardly unpacked a presentation titled: "Pornography: The Silent Christian Killer." And how could I forget the 70-year-old key note speaker claiming to have cracked the code on Millennials.

I skipped out on my final session to grab a latte and find some wisdom. Standing in the bookstore, letting the iced coffee cool my body temperature, I desperately scanned the covers like a puzzle builder trying to find his missing piece. No doubt I skimmed half-heartedly past hundreds of titles written by talented people. But the homogeny of the subjects startled me. Sure, we all could use some deep, spiritual wisdom. And yes, research on faith trends and team building are valid. But, that's not what I wanted. I was searching for a text that showcased the messiness of religion, because I was a bit of a mess. Or the raw, lived experience of the skeptic; the person who might say, "Seriously, you've got to stop shouting 'Hallelujah' and 'Amen' every five seconds. It's freaking me out."

I left the bookstore with a copy of C. S. Lewis' *Mere Christianity* - which I never finished because, well, it's just not that funny. Upon returning home, I grabbed my wife's 10-year-old MacBook (with the broken charger prong that kept falling out of the socket) and began typing an outline. Maybe this story should never have been written. There's some crude language, adult situations, baffling character behavior, and a reconciliation that's hard to believe. Obviously, I patterned it after another fairly popular Christian book – one that has been argued over for centuries.

Here's hoping I don't piss God off. Although the wrath of humans seems a lot worse these days. I imagine the big guy upstairs might just chuckle with a hearty belly-laugh. And right now, we could all use a bit of levity in our lives.

# THE
# CHURCH
# WORKER

A NOVEL BY
## DAVE DIETRICH

Cover design by Matthew Washburn

Text layout by Clark Kenyon

Editing consultant Jordana Berliner

ISBN: 978-1-7349405-0-3 (paperback)
ISBN: 978-1-7349405-1-0 (ebook)
ISBN: 978-1-7349405-2-7 (audiobook)

Manufactured in the United States of America

www.dietrichwrites.com

*Does God have a sense of humor? He must have if he created us.*
—Jackie Gleason

# 1

# Revelation

December 4, 2017

I practiced all the things I would say. Now I can't find the words. I keep waiting for you to go first. The silence is killing me. No more nails to chew off, and my own foot tapping is starting to drive me crazy. I'm not sure why I always try to fill the quiet moments, the pauses between conversation. But I don't want to sit here in this uncomfortable chair and ramble. Given the setting and situation, maybe there's an opportunity to treat this like confession—even though you're the last person I would ever expect to play the priest.

I've never confided in an official priest; someone with "Father" prefixed to their name. Always wondered how they cram into a claustrophobic stall, day after day, doling out advice and absolution. I couldn't do it. My words would choke on tears during the desperate cries of the bereaved. And my laughter would betray me when the confessant said something like: "My wife spanked me last night and I kind of liked it. Is that a sin?" Religion can certainly be bizarre at times. I might have a few opinions on the subject. I know you do.

So, let's talk about God. He's an interesting character, that creator of the universe. You still believe he exists? Lately, I feel like he's been having a bit of fun with me. A lot of people say God has a sense of humor. I used to find this ironic because—from what I knew of the Bible—he seemed to spend an inordinate amount of time drowning folks, setting things on fire, and cutting off parts of peoples' penises.

But now I work for him, I guess. I never told you how that ended up happening, did I? It's a long story. In fact, I'm not sure I've told anyone. Bits and pieces, sure. Never the entire saga of scandals, salvation, and sewage in the sanctuary. Oh, and I can't forget about the carnivorous goat.

Okay, this'll be good. If I'm going to do justice to the telling, I'll have to cover some ground. We haven't had a conversation like this for quite a while. Maybe ever. Let's start with this: there were about a hundred reasons why I almost *didn't* work for God.

I had written church off as a viable institution for my entire adult life. Remembering events from my childhood, I now understand why. For instance, I acquired a few palpable nightmares thanks to "Judgment House," that fun little religious twist on Halloween. I don't remember all the rooms, but I know it culminated in a pitch-black passageway with doors locked at both ends. Nice church folks pumped heaters into the long slender hallway, and volunteer actors screamed in an attempt to create Hell on Earth. I peed my pants. Then, I walked out into the light and met a man dressed like Jesus. And after reciting a little prayer, I got "saved" by one of the preachers. I was nine.

By my teen years, I became acutely aware that, for me, something was unsettling about organized religion. I was in the throes of awkward puberty, attempting to mask my insecurities. And if life was a class, half the time, I thought I was failing it.

This juxtaposed against the halls and pews of church, which felt like an exclusive country club. People in crisp clothes, keeping up enviable pretenses. The adults in church seemed to have life figured out in ways that I didn't—that is, until the avalanche of deceit and dirty deeds behind the scenes of my upbringing came crashing down. As it turns out, good Christian adulterers, tax evaders, and liars hid behind glossy masks. Two people even got caught conjugating in the baptismal pool after hours. I guess that's why parents tell you not to swallow the pool water.

And what about the interesting language proliferated by the numerous evangelists of my youth? "You are either the righteous or the wicked," they would say. "When the devil comes for you, you must rebuke him!" "Repent and be saved!" I don't remember anyone outside of church using words like these. I can't think of a scenario where any of it would qualify as colloquial conversation in other settings. "If a man approaches you at a bar, and you dislike his advances… you must rebuke him!" Hmm, that actually sounds more natural than I thought it would.

Either way, a mixture of intrigue, confusion, and fear dotted my early introduction to religion. Which begs the question: why in the world did I… Joe Dasch… a truly accomplished sinner with ambitions to conquer corporate giants, take a job working for a church?

I mostly blame Pastor Jake. He first approached me almost three years ago, after I had returned from a vacation in Mexico with Layla and several friends. We had drunk enough rum to fill a pirate ship and had raunchy married-sex in very un-Christian-like ways. I was still jetlagged and hungover when the pastor approached me after the service. Laughter churned in my belly when Pastor Jake mentioned the idea of me working with him at the church. But I choked it down for fear that the squeezing of my abdomen might make me throw up on a holy man.

Only a few months earlier, after a lot of debate and false starts, I had succumbed to Layla's insistence and begrudgingly agreed to go to church with her. I unexpectedly began to wake up a dormant faith, something I had buried for many years. But let's be clear: no one would've described me as a ministry man. I hadn't prayed much other than over the occasional meal. I wasn't reading the Bible as often as I should. And, thanks to my Pa Paw, the phrase "Well, shit damn!" got a lot of play in my vocabulary for a while. That old church deacon never was one to mince words.

Regardless, my life was about to be blown off the course I had painstakingly planned and chartered. At the time Pastor Jake got his hooks into me, I had been working for less than two years in a V.P. role that paid well over six figures. I relished the prestige of the position and focused on the accumulations of a well-constructed nest egg. We were living a comfortable existence in a mid-century modern starter home with neighbors who did lots of yard work on a street with lots of trees. Yeah, I had become one of those insufferable people who described their neighborhood as having "gorgeous tree-lined streets."

I also commissioned an old door to be made into a dining room table, purchased forty-five square feet of quartz countertops for Layla, and spent three months trying to DIY a half bath using only how-to videos on YouTube. Notice anything different about this thumb? Yeah, a small part of it is missing. Thanks, *HGTV*.

The point is I thought I had a lot going for me: a rising career, a great family, and a red SUV with a third row for my one child. Would I be willing to risk it all to go work for an institution that, until quite recently, I considered to be unnecessary and outdated? I didn't think that would be a prudent decision. Plus, I wondered what working for a church even looked like. I presumed there was just a lot of praying and hoping for the best. Surely, I would struggle to support my family. And how would I explain to my friends that I had given up a strategic role at a burgeoning company to go work for the Holy Spirit?

Somehow the pastor saw something in me that I did not. And the best pastors are very convincing—they're kind of like Jedi Masters. And Pastor Jake is one of the best. I'm talking about the original Jedi, by the way, the ones from back in the day. Not those cartoonish goons from the mostly terrible reboots. It's a shame what they did to Skywalker and company.

To draw a religious comparison, it's like they took the Bible and said, "Hey, let's turn Jesus back into an angry carpenter and have Mary float into space. Wouldn't that be great?" Uh, no. No, it wouldn't.

Anyhow, Pastor Jake wore me down for several weeks, but I finally caved after my 17th pro/con list. And to this day I can't tell you why. I didn't receive a divine whisper in my ear. No angel visited me. And for a fairly logical person, this was perhaps the most illogical decision I had ever made.

Over the next two years, I was an integral part of the inner workings of a church. I witnessed extraordinary acts of kindness and generosity. I saw the way families leaned on their faith when grieving the death of a loved one. I also walked in on a homeless man sharting inside an old shed which happened to be on the church property. He was tearing a page out of Leviticus when I found him. I don't think it was for reading.

I got to be part of the chaos of performing fifty-two services a year, and the celebrations of the lives transformed. I learned that many people who work for churches are smart and passionate about what they do. I also once heard a youth pastor belt out "I Touch Myself" by The Divinyls at a karaoke bar. Given his vocation, it was a poor choice and one that could've done without the hand gestures.

These last two years have been a mixed bag, to say the least. But I don't regret my decision. I've learned to appreciate the hilarious fallibility of organized religion. I've also learned to appreciate the struggle of faith and the vibrant community made possible by people who go to church. My cynicism was heartily reinforced in some instances, but my optimism unexpectedly broadened in many others.

Did I find the meaning of life? Did I really discover God? Do I still think, on the whole, that Christians are about as nutty as a porta-potty at a peanut festival? We'll see.

# 2

# two are better
# than one...

To give you the full story, I'm going to have to talk about the Backstreet Boys. Yes, the boy band from the nineties and early 2000s. They're my butterfly effect. And Layla was the first ripple. Although her ripple was more a tidal wave. Might be helpful to tell you how Layla and I met.

In my mid-twenties, I got swept up in the explosion of 21st-century dating. I had a profile on almost every available app or website offering the opportunity to connect with people I was too nervous to talk to in person. So many late nights were illuminated by flashes of my phone swiping through digital catalogs of women. I was amazed by how hard it was to find compatibility despite the 40-mile radius of singles (or those claiming to be "single") who were accessible via a simple tap of the finger.

I hit a breaking point when Amy, whom I'd met on plentyoffish.com, told me she was confused as to why I hadn't slept with her yet. She went on to talk a lot about wanting a baby really soon and not being able to waste time. She even uttered the word "impregnate" right around the time dessert was served. Normally hearing the word "impregnate" on a third date gets me all hot and bothered. But the syllables didn't thrum my libido this time. Instead, I momentarily daydreamed of Amy on top of me in a queen-sized bed, yelling, "Give me your seed!" in an eerie low-pitched voice. I promptly faked an illness, left the restaurant, then went home and canceled all of my dating accounts. Less than a week later, I met Layla.

\*\*\*

You probably don't know this about me, but I love karaoke. It's one of those guilty pleasures that I don't feel guilty about. I thoroughly enjoy watching brave souls get up and sing off-key versions of popular songs in front of complete strangers. I don't have much time for it anymore, but a few years ago, it was my go-to entertainment. I loved karaoke partly because—being from the South—I unabashedly love blue-collar people. There tends to be a lot of them at karaoke bars. But mostly I want to get on stage and sing two specific songs: "Sweet Caroline" by Neil Diamond and "Everybody" by the Backstreet Boys. Clearly, I'm a conflicted human being.

Only five days after declaring that I needed a nice long break from the dating scene, my friend Brian Fetzer invited me to a little dive called The Last Stop. Fetzer is a guy who I'm fairly certain lives on a diet of red meat and Budweiser and sometimes talks about how hot my sixty-one-year-old mom is. Also, I find him to smell a bit like someone who has passed gas and then tried to cover it up with a tropical Febreze spray. Anyone who has ever shared an office restroom would be familiar with this odor cocktail, which leads to a lack of respect for fellow employees.

However, Fetzer's unfiltered, lackadaisical personality makes him one of the most honest and endearing people I've ever encountered. He's always interesting to be around. Plus, it was a Friday night, and The Last Stop was hosting karaoke; that was all I needed to know.

I met him there around 9:00 p.m. From the outside, the bar had an unassuming, grungy appearance. The wedge created by the adjoining storefronts made me think I was about to enter a claustrophobic space with low ceilings pinning down a smoky odor. But the exterior falsely represented what I saw inside. The building had to be 10,000 square feet. There were large rooms containing pool tables, darts, and other bar games. These all connected back to the small entry space, which is where I saw the karaoke man setting up. Most of the action seemed to be crackling out of this tiny space.

People began to cram in next to the long bar running the length of the left wall, or they lingered near a few closely placed cocktail tables. Almost everything in the place felt sticky: the floors, the walls, the glassware, the waitress. I remember one patron saying, "It smells like shame in here!" It certainly did not seem like the kind of place where I'd meet a gorgeous woman who would forever change the course of my life. I did, however, think Fetzer's future wife could easily be in the mix.

Layla walked in at 10:25 p.m. Seriously, I checked the time; she was that striking. It's funny; you never know what's going to draw you to a person. I joke about the bar, but there were plenty of other attractive women. Something in the core of my body changed, though, when I saw Layla. Her natural beauty wasn't masked by a heavy load of makeup. Her eyes were green and inviting. Her clothes were sexy, but not desperate. When she laughed, it seemed she didn't care how agape her mouth was or who was watching. Her every motion looked effortless but intentional. I needed to find a way to talk to this woman.

This is precisely the type of situation where Fetzer comes in handy. I love him in part because he has no scruples about approaching complete strangers. The downside is he has no filter. And, as I mentioned, he kind of smells. I figured I had no shot with this girl anyway, so what could I lose. A simple nudge and a dart of the eyes were all I needed to deploy my furry, smelly friend to pave the way.

Somehow his unkempt fashion and endearing demeanor won over Layla and her three friends. He gave me the signal to join them, which by the way, was him hooking his thumbs together and making an exaggerated flapping motion with his hands. The stubby fingers were taunting me, "Come on over little butterfly; the meadow is safe." I probably deserved it.

I stumbled through the crowd, nerves rattling like a baby goat dropped into shark-infested waters. The seats were all taken, so I simply posted up in what I hoped was a suave standing position. Layla was right next to me, and she was even more amazing up close. I would catch her glimpsing at me through pauses in the conversation. Most of the chatter consisted of a heated debate between Fetzer and one of Layla's friends. It was something about which type of alcohol made you less fat. I finally had to say something.

"Hi, I'm Joe. What's your name?"

Layla and I learned we were both transplants who had recently moved into the city. We'd each broken off serious relationships within the past year, and surprisingly, we found common ground on our strange affinity for Chinese buffets. I was from the South, and she was from the rural Midwest (which are basically the same places). She laughed genuinely at my dumb jokes, and I traced her lips every time she spoke.

Men don't ever talk about this, but there is absolutely a euphoria that overtakes us during encounters with certain women. Not the kind that happens when there seems to be mutual admiration. It's not when we score a phone number that we didn't think we could get. It's not even when we realize someone probably wants to sleep with us. It's an unexplainable epiphany that causes our heart to shoot up into our brains. Such an encounter might happen at first glance, on the first date, after six months, or after six years. But it only happens with one woman out of 100,000. I was having one of those moments with Layla.

I glanced at my phone and realized I'd been talking to her for almost an hour, and midnight was fast approaching. Time was irrelevant. I could've talked to her until the sun peeked into the windows of The Last Stop—if only they'd let us stay that long. Then I stupidly asked, "So what are you gals doing here anyway?"

"Well, these are my coworkers. It's Katie's birthday, and she *loves* karaoke. We started this little soiree at about 5:30. I'm well past my original self-imposed curfew, but I promised someone I'd meet him here."

She kept going. Unfortunately.

"If I'm being honest, I've been talking to this guy, and I told him this was our last stop—no pun intended—and to meet me here around ten or eleven if he made it out. He should have been here a while ago, so I have no idea if he's going to show up."

I wanted to tell her the guy she had been talking to was a known serial killer who would dismember his victims and store their remains in children's playground equipment. But that probably would've killed the vibe. Instead, I decided to try and wait him out. The Last Stop closed at 1:30 a.m., so I had some time. Fifteen minutes later, my nemesis showed up. His name was Scott.

I hated Scott. He was this good-looking, regal stallion of a man with broad shoulders and a mane of hair that he tossed brazenly from side to side. He strode into the bar to claim his prized mare. My whole body deflated when Layla signaled him over. The three of us created a kind of isosceles triangle, with Layla and I forming the base and Scott slowly closing the circumference with his stealthy moves and cool jacket. As I was about to become the third wheel, I heard a voice over the speaker system: "And next up we have Joe D.! Can I get Joe D. to the stage?"

Somewhere along the way, I had filled out a tiny, damp slip of paper and handed it to the karaoke DJ. Now I was being summoned by the microphone. There's this interesting moment in karaoke when the DJ calls someone to the stage. First, everyone is curious about what Joe D. looks like. In this case, as you know, he was a tallish, pale, white guy with auburn hair who may have been an athlete at one time, but now just goes bowling every once in a while. Then, there's the intrigue of what song Joe D. is going to sing. I'm assuming most folks try to judge the song choice based on appearances. If that's the case, the majority of the room probably thought they were in for either a sappy ballad or an angsty '90s alternative rock song. But I didn't care about the audience. The most dazzling woman I'd ever met was being wooed by Scott the serial killer.

The big reveal in karaoke is before the first note is ever sung. It's when the name of the song is flashed on the screen behind the stage, and the crowd takes silent bets on how good or bad the rendition will be. Often the audience has an idea of how it's going to go, but performances vary wildly. And some songs seem so out of reach or ill-fitting to the person picking up the microphone that the entire room grins with anticipation. Any time I do Backstreet Boys, people perk up and wonder what the hell is about to happen.

I launched into the first chorus.

"Everybody!..."

The place went wild. I'm not a rock star or a recording artist, but there are a couple of songs that—for some reason—just fit my wheelhouse, and this is one of them. Or perhaps I get pity credits for simply attempting an outdated boy band tune in the first place. Either way, at that moment, I played to the crowd with every awkward dance move and almost on-key note I could muster. I was hoping Layla might appreciate a guy who wasn't afraid to make a complete fool of himself in a sultry, irresistible, and borderline offensive way. But each time I looked over, she seemed to be enthralled with Scott.

There can't be many moments as dejecting as singing a boy band song on a dirty karaoke stage while you watch the girl of your dreams start a relationship with another man. I was basically serenading the two of them. I faked an upbeat persona as long as I could, but I let the last few lyrics go unsung. I abruptly handed the microphone back to the karaoke guy and headed toward the bar. It was time. Who was I kidding? My wingman was a drunken sasquatch, and Layla was out of my league. I needed to call it a night.

I signaled for my tab to be closed, signed the wet receipt, and slid my credit card back into my wallet. I dropped the pen on the counter and turned to leave. Layla appeared out of nowhere, smiling up at me. Flustered, I said, "Hey, what happened to Scott?" It's going to sound like I'm making this up, but I swear to you, she took a step forward, reached her hand up around my neck, and pulled me down to kiss her.

It was primal. It was passionate. It happened less than ten feet away from Scott. When we finally unlocked lips, I looked over to find his nasty scowl bearing down on me. But Layla gently pulled my chin back to her. Then she said, "You are the strangest man I've ever met." She gave me one more kiss for good measure. Scott had one less victim to claim.

Layla and I got swept up in one another after the karaoke episode. We dated for almost a year, which led to us moving in together, which led to her mom hating me (for religious reasons), which led to me getting Layla pregnant. Okay, so we actually got pregnant after we were married. And that's really where this whole thing began. The conversation you and I never had, starts with the birth of Rose.

# 3

# ...a child is born

Layla and I arrived at the hospital on July 5th, 2014, for the scheduled inducement that would bring our first child into this world. We were both tired but excited. We would be answering to the names "Mommy" and "Daddy." There would be no more distended belly, no more emotional roller coasters, and no more third trimester attempts at intimacy—which were really attempts to coax the baby out. Our perfect little creation would be here soon.

Thirty-four hours later and the only thing saving us was our mutual loathing of the baby catcher—I don't know what else to call the nurse who helps catch the baby. Layla had been sitting three-quarters upright for what seemed like an eternity, hadn't eaten anything other than broth and popsicles, and had been prodded and explored by at least five other medical professionals. The last nurse arrived—the one ensuring the baby came out head first—and held things in check while we waited for our obstetrician. She just kept going on and on about the beautiful crowning head of our daughter.

I realize some guys want to get up close and personal to document the experience. It's as if their wife's lady parts are somehow going to produce a Sundance Festival award-winning short film. That's not me. I was shoulders-up the whole way. I wanted to retain good memories for below the waist. Also, when does one watch a birth video anyway? Is it something you just break out at a bar mitzvah or a game night with friends that gets a little out of hand? And what's the commentary?

"Look at the size of that baby! Wow, that looks like it hurts!" To even the playing field, maybe wives should be allowed to film their husbands' colonoscopies.

The baby catcher kept urging me to get down there and take a look.

"Daddy, you really need to see this. She's *beautiful!*"

"Uh, I'm good up here."

"No, seriously. It's amazing. You'll regret it. It's your only chance to see it!"

I began to waver. "How much blood is there?"

Was I a bad dad if I didn't watch my baby come out? Were the other dads better than me? But as I questioned myself, I remembered Layla and I were a united front regarding my physical position during the birth. In fact, her request had been quite specific. She did not want my head and the baby's head to be in the same proximity until the baby's head was out and clean of birth debris. I was going to honor that request. But the baby catcher kept on. "No, no, it's beautiful. She's getting ready to slide out soon. Come on, Daddy; you have to take a look!"

Maybe it was the flippant use of the word "slide" or her fluffy conversational tone. Whatever the case, Layla suddenly shot up. "Damn it! He doesn't want to see it, lady. And quit calling him 'Daddy!' And get this baby out of me!"

I loved how she snapped at the woman for calling me "Daddy." Sure, she probably shouldn't have cursed at the nurse trying to deliver her child. And yes, the grizzled voice and blood-shot eyes made me wonder if Layla's head was about to spin 360 degrees while she started speaking in tongues. But it was an honest moment. My sweaty, pale, half-paralyzed wife was completely vulnerable, and yet somehow still came to my defense. It was raw and messy, and I loved her for it. I started to raise my hand to high-five her but thought better of it.

The baby catcher didn't say anything else. She just caught the baby.

\*\*\*

Rose changed everything. I suppose that's a bit cliché. One minute we had no child, and then suddenly we were parents. Obviously, everything changed. There were many sleepless nights. There were interminable shrill cries which drove us to the brink of insanity. The smell of poop seemed ever-present. The breastfeeding was difficult. The daycare search was nerve-wracking. And gone were the spontaneous dinner dates and the late nights full of questionable decisions. That's all normal for a lot of new parents, I suppose.

I couldn't have known at the time how much little Rose would spark a different kind of change, one that would catapult me toward something completely unexpected. A few months after the birth, baby boot camp began to let up, and some semblance of a routine and normalcy returned to our lives. Layla started to ask questions I wasn't prepared to answer.

I remember December being unusually cold that year, even for the Midwest. The elemental chill creeping through our house brought us closer together, both physically and emotionally. We talked a lot and needed to stay close for warmth. Once Rose finally conceded the fight and went to sleep each night, Layla would snuggle up to me to take advantage of my extreme body heat. I say extreme for a reason. There's a comic book superhero called the Human Torch. I'm a poor man's version of that guy. My sweltering bod is comforting in the winter season and kind of gross in July.

One blustery night just before Christmas, Layla decided to make her move. "Alright, hubs, how are we going to raise this kid?"

"Well, babe, we should probably continue feeding it, keep it dry, give it clothing—that sort of thing."

"You know what I mean, Joe. What kinds of things do we want to expose her to?"

"Well, since you asked, my plan is to keep her sheltered for about the next twenty years. Maybe we can medically engineer some kind of horrible chronic acne problem that lasts throughout her teen and college years—I'm talking boiled-pepperoni-type acne, the kind that drives the boys away and forces her to stay indoors and study a lot. Then at twenty-five, we can begin reducing the dosage and eventually let her start to date people."

"You're a disturbed human being. Also, the acne thing probably wouldn't work; you boys are pretty resilient. But seriously, we need to talk about how we're going to parent together. You know… how to discipline, how to socialize, how to educate, and even what kind of spirituality we would introduce to her."

The impetus for the conversation was now becoming clear to me. Layla had talked to me about going to church for years, even before we were married. I was fairly entrenched in my stance that corporate worship was an unnecessary evil. Even so, oddly, I still considered myself a Christian by default. I just didn't go to a house of worship. Or pray. Or read the Bible. Or talk to people about God. But I was an American. In God we trust, right?

"I'm assuming you want to have the conversation about religion. You've heard my thoughts on the subject. Do we really want to go down this road again?"

"Look, I know this isn't easy for you, Joe. I just think it's important. If we don't talk about it now, it's just going to fester. It'll be something I start to resent. You know this is important to me."

"Babe, I think it's great that you have a strong sense of faith or belief or whatever. But you're right—it's hard for me.

I watched the so-called church turn its back on my mom when she got divorced. My brother got ostracized when he didn't fit the mold. The freaking pastor wouldn't send a letter to my cousin, who was in prison. The list goes on."

"I know, I know. But how long can you hold onto that stuff? Eventually, you have to learn how to let go and realize not everyone or every place is like that."

"You didn't have the same experiences I did growing up. It was pretty messed up. Plus, I feel like things are going really well for us right now. Why do we need to disrupt our lives with some archaic tradition that's hypocritical and exclusive?"

As in most long-term relationships, she knew my buttons, and I knew hers. These kinds of conversations can go from friendly domestic dialogue to Armageddon in a flash. We had learned how to fight constructively for the most part, but every now and then, we strapped on our helmets and went to war. She decided to lob the first bomb. "Look, I get you have some kind of church PTSD, but you can sound pretty condescending sometimes for a person who talks about hypocrites. I mean, this could be a good way for you to meet some new people, maybe some other parents who get what we're going through. Honestly, it would be awesome if you found anyone to hang out with besides Jimmy and Fetzer."

"Wait, what do you have against Jimmy and Fetzer? I thought this was supposed to be about Rose, by the way."

"It's about all of us. And I just don't see how hanging onto those drinking buddies is doing you any good. It's not challenging you in any way. I'm just asking you to think about it. Think about how we're going to raise our daughter, and how you and I are going to stay connected."

"You just don't like that I have a man-crush on Fetzer and his extravagant facial hair," I said, attempting a cautious grin.

Layla scowled. "Come on, Joe, I don't want you to joke your way out of this. I'd like to have a real conversation."

"Okay, fine. You want to know what I really think? Those people are fake, Layla. They're *fake*, and I don't want our daughter growing up to be some Sunday morning Stepford Wife who can't hold an original thought or have an open-minded conversation."

"Wow. Do you even hear yourself? You sort of just condemned the entire Christian community in one swoop. And particularly Christian women, one of whom happens to be lying next to you." She rolled away from me and sprang off the bed. "And by the way, Joseph Joshua Dasch, things are not perfect. We have plenty of our own issues, but you want to act like you've got it all figured out. I don't want to keep having this conversation for the next twenty years. I won't do it. Can't you see something's missing? Are you that blind? Damn it, wake up, Joe!"

Then, Layla farted. I'm sure it was instigated by the jerky motion she made jumping out of bed. I'd been learning about post-pregnancy bodies and how they often betrayed themselves.

"Did you just curse me, and then fart at me?" I said, my defenses weakening through pinched laughter.

"Yes, and I'm still mad at you," she said, snorting a bit. Another audible whoosh escaped her butt, this one probably from trying to hold in the laughter. "What's wrong with me?!" she said.

There would be no Round 2 for us. This fight was over. We began laughing hysterically. I was pressed into the pillow, trying to muffle the sound that I was certain would awaken Rose at any moment. Layla was crunched into a ball on the floor by the dresser. Her face was buried between her knees.

Suddenly she popped up again. "Oh my God, I peed myself! My vagina just ain't right!"

I lost it. No amount of fabric or cotton could contain the cackling my body was producing as I saw the trickling stain begin to darken her green sweatpants. She, too, had lost all restraint. With only shaky fingers and cupped hands attempting to muzzle her giggles, it was just a matter of time. We heard faint sounds coming from Rose's crib, and then gradually, the crying started.

I took care of our baby while Layla looked for a fresh pair of pajama pants. Eventually, I got Rose back to sleep. Our bodies were tired from the combination of anger, laughter, and the release of bodily functions. We let sleep deprivation do its work. She went out first, and I followed shortly after. I don't think we said another word. I slept quite well that night.

Layla and I didn't revisit our conversation until after Christmas. I had a lot of deadlines to meet before the end of the year, and she was preparing to return to work in a few weeks. But primarily it was because we were hosting Christmas for both sides of the family. After all, we had the newborn. We knew it would take a well-stocked reserve of wits and patience to get through it. Thus, we pressed pause on our own struggles for the moment.

I could say a lot about the Fisher-Davis-Conklin-Dasch holiday extravaganza, but perhaps a recap is best. Here are some highlights:

1. The mothers-in-law demonstrated black belt level passive-aggressiveness, which almost culminated in a fight to the death—death by sulking, backhanded compliments, and indirect hostility.
2. The fathers-in-law attempted to escape the passive-aggressive battle their wives were having. They drank eleven gin and tonics, then tried to play darts. I requested spackling as a belated Christmas gift to fill the innumerable holes in my basement wall.
3. Layla's sister and her husband requested Mexican food for every meal other than Christmas dinner. An odious bean and cheese smell soon began to emanate throughout our home.
4. Rick was high 50 percent of the time; I've never been more envious of my brother.

I appreciate each of these people individually, but collectively, they are a hurricane sweeping through a bad soap opera. Family gatherings remind me of bachelorette parties. Separately, the people are mostly sane and easy to get along with. Then they're forced together under the guise of "celebration," and the party goes off the rails. Before you know it, someone's phallic-shaped straw is jamming them in the gums, and your sister slips a disc trying to ride the mechanical bull.

Despite their antics and unpredictable personalities, our families have almost always been supportive. Well, most of them. I've always struggled with the relationship dichotomy that families tend to highlight. They're the first people we criticize, and yet the first we call in times of need. I guess it's just nice to have someone to call in a time of need.

Anyhow, Christmas happened, and New Year's Eve seemed to hurry right after. In previous years, we might have selected from a buffet of options for tomfoolery. Instead, as freshly fatigued parents, we consumed a half bottle of Korbel Extra Dry and watched the West Coast ball drop, so we could get to bed by 10:01 p.m. instead of midnight. This was considered "partying."

January 1st also came and went without much fanfare. I don't remember anything of note. It wasn't like January 1st of 2000 when I awoke with anxiety, wondering if parts of the universe had exploded thanks to the world wide web not being able to convert nines to zeros. Do you remember that? Talk about people excited for the second coming of Christ. Fortunately, New Year's Day 2015 was boring for us—another day in life simply chugging along.

January 2nd, 2015 was a different day. It was the day Ohio State upset Alabama to reach the National Championship in the first-ever college football playoff. It was the first time I could remember having a five-day weekend since I started working as an adult. And it was the day I decided to give God another try.

Since the birth of Rose, I had embraced the life of an early riser… well, at least much earlier than the 7 a.m. weekday / 9 a.m. weekend ritual I'd practiced throughout much of my adult life. Saying I was reluctant to adopt this new existence is a massive understatement. I love sleep. How can you not? Lying prostrate on a soft mass of springs, foam, or feathers (or water, for really creepy folks) is a heavenly experience. It is estimated we sleep a third of our lives; I would gladly double that.

With Rose, we never knew what we were getting. Some days it was 3 a.m., screaming like a boiling lobster. Other times she wouldn't wake until well past 7 a.m. Unfortunately, often those were also the days we would wake up at 4 a.m., wonder if she was still breathing, rush into her room to check on her, and then just sit on the floor playing on our phones until she woke up.

The morning Layla finally got me to cave in, Rose had made her cooing noises just after 6 a.m. Let me just say that, for me, there's a big psychological difference between 5 a.m. and 6 a.m. For starters, the number 6 has a nice shape to it. If you turn it horizontal, it's kind of smiling at you. At 6 a.m., coffee shops are opening their doors. Birds are chirping. Flowers are beginning to bloom. The world is coming to life. At 5 a.m., it is as dark as a black hole. Infomercials are still trying to sell the latest presidential coin collection. Late night bars have just cleaned the last of the vomit off their floors. Birds are falling from trees. Flowers are dying.

So, by waking after 6 a.m., I was in a fairly decent mood,

which boded well for my wife. We decided to make breakfast together. Although I wasn't a morning person, I had discovered a love for home-cooked breakfasts. It became an art form for me: eggs cracked and whisked, then poured into a large skillet on low heat; strips of maple bacon laid out over a bath of olive oil and fried until they were crisp, but not burnt; strawberries rinsed in cold water until they gleamed; ripe bananas sliced and mixed into the strawberries; fresh coffee brewed with cinnamon and cream. Breakfast had become a Zen experience.

Even though there were only three of us, I made a huge breakfast; we could always polish it off over the weekend. Rose was restricted to eggs and bananas, but I loved watching her eat. She couldn't use a fork yet, so she'd use her fingers to grab at the various items spread out across her highchair tray. The chance of the food entering her mouth was about 50/50.

After breakfast, we were getting ready for nap #1. Everything for parents of young children is planned around naps. We played for an hour or so and watched Elmo sing a song about himself, followed by Mickey Mouse doing something called the "hotdog dance." If you ask me, it was all a bit unimpressive. Layla then cradled Rose in the beige glider, swishing back and forth with much less creaking than the old rocking chair we'd thrown out via Craigslist. After ten minutes, Rose was out.

Between naps, there were several duties: wash dishes, start laundry, sweep floors, pick up toys, go to Home Depot, etc. etc. Our pediatrician advised us to sleep when our daughter slept to stay sane and rested. But what did he know? He only went to school for like twenty-seven years. We typically ignored his advice, often to our detriment.

But this day was a bit different. While there was no sleeping, there were also no chores. No trips to Walgreens or Walmart or any other Wal-store. Layla poured me a cup of coffee, added some cinnamon and hazelnut cream, and placed it on the table of the three-seasons room just off the kitchen.

She poured herself a mimosa, so I knew she meant business, and then asked me to sit with her.

"Okay, now that both of our crazy families are gone, it's time to talk."

I winced. My defenses were down. The morning had been great. The scrumptious breakfast still lay heavy in my belly. She had given me cinnamon. I was vulnerable.

"Hubs, we have to make a path here. On the one hand, I love so many things in my life right now. I love you. I love Rose. I love our experiences."

I braced for the self-rebuttal.

"But I'm not entirely happy either. Seems we're checking all the boxes in pursuit of the so-called 'perfect life,' but what's getting left behind? We're all excited about your new job and the new house and the new car. I so appreciate these things, but they're not what really lights me up. I'm proud of you for what you've been able to accomplish, but if we lose sight of each other, it's all for nothing."

I tend to talk a lot, but this seemed to be one of those times where I needed to listen. So, I just kept my trap shut. She continued.

"There are a lot of reasons to celebrate our life. But what do they add up to? I want to be comfortable and safe and financially secure just as much as the next person. But is that the entirety of our goals and dreams? If it is, then something's terribly wrong."

There was a long pause. I guessed she was waiting for me.

"I'm not sure what you want me to say, babe."

"Tell me you will at least consider that there's something more than this. Tell me you have felt restless but can't quite figure out why. Tell me you're isolated more often than you'd like to admit."

"Are you trying to psychoanalyze me there, darlin'?"

"Hey, whatever it takes."

"Okay, just don't fart on me again."

I wondered if she'd chastise me, but her lips pursed to a slight grin. "I can't make any promises," she said. Layla stared down at the table, studying the chipped paint and the curve of the wood. "I believe there's an intelligent design to everything, Joe. I don't think we're the result of a random explosion or a series of coincidences. I believe in God." She looked back up before continuing. "I fell in love with you faster than expected. I tricked myself into thinking I could bury the faith conversation and unearth it at a later date. But it never happened. You've held onto your pain and disdain, and I let the excuses pile up. It's time to let that go. I really need you with me on this. As uncomfortable as it might be, I have to recommit to my faith, and I want my husband with me."

"Okay," I said, relenting.

I didn't try to fight or object in the numerous ways I could have. In the back of my mind, I'm sure I thought this was a fleeting promise. I'd play along for a brief time, then this would fizzle out, and things would go back to normal. But I at least owed it to Layla to give it a shot. And, truth be told, my nerves lit up at the prospect of meeting God again on his turf.

I imagined entering a religious service for the first time in over a decade. I could only come up with flashes of the church from my youth. The sharp geometric shapes of a towering angular sanctuary. Stadium seating. Playing tic-tac-toe with Rick during the sermon. Mom's shoulder pads under her blue suit jacket. A choir of at least 50 people draped in slick robes. And, according to the microphone booming out into the sound system, a need to "be saved."

Lost in this thought, I absentmindedly reached for my mug and knocked my coffee over.

# 4

# church shopping...

On the second Sunday of January in 2015, I stepped into a church of my own volition for the first time in thirteen years. Aside from weddings and funerals, I hadn't purposely darkened the door of a worship service since I left college to begin "adulting." I'm sure you've heard the term at some point. We made the word up so young adults would feel accomplished every time they made a car payment or put $10 in their 401k. In my early twenties, I drove a fifteen-year-old Dodge Neon, so I didn't have $10 to put into my non-existent retirement account. And I never went to church.

Layla had almost always been a faithful churchgoer, even during her partying days. I'll admit, her flaws are why I ultimately acquiesced to reenter the church world again at all. I knew at least one other person in the joint would be pretty far from perfect, and that gave me some measure of solace. Layla was answering the pull back to her faith. She didn't have a home church anymore, though. So, we found one on Yelp with a 4.5-star rating. It was called The Rock.

I wasn't sure I liked the name. All I kept thinking about was Dwayne Johnson's catchphrase from when he was a wrestler. I imagined walking up to the church and being greeted with: "Can you smell what The Rock is cookin'?" Perhaps this was one of those cool, post-modern hipster churches. We'd start the morning with synthesizers, smoke machines, and banjos. Then some guy in skinny jeans, a V-neck, and a blazer would come out and say something like: "Y'all ready to get your Jesus on?! Yeah, God is for *real*, y'all! This worship is gonna *be off the chain!* Hashtag Jesus rocks!" <mic drop> Then there would be explosions from confetti cannons. Maybe I let my imagination get the better of me.

The church was a formidable size, easily a story taller than the adjacent strip mall with an Urgent Care that clearly used to be a Blockbuster Video, and outdated retailers like a Big Lots and a Radio Shack. That's not what threw me off, though. What I couldn't understand was the construction of the building. So much of it seemed to be comprised of glass. A wall of glass broke up the concrete façade at the entry, topped by a two-story arched window. Rows of stained glass flanked each side and ran half the length of the building. And glass sculptures, in shades of purple and green, adorned the flower beds. The mid-morning sun was bouncing off the panes annoyingly; my hand, like a car visor, couldn't find the correct angle to block the sharp beams of light.

I kept thinking this church had the most ironic name—one

toss of a decent-sized rock looked like it would bring the whole thing tumbling down. I'll concede, however, calling the church "The Glass" probably wouldn't have been as effective.

Now that we had arrived, I began to have unwelcome sensations. I go through a strange metamorphosis any time I don't want to be somewhere. My shoulders become sluggish, my mouth curves slightly downward, and my legs labor with each step as if my feet have turned into cinder blocks. I used to experience this on my walk from the parking lot to the cubicle farm at my first job as an insurance adjuster. Or when Layla drags me to watch a romantic comedy. Or on the way to the gym sometimes. Or basically any toddler's birthday party. And now it was happening at church.

I was sweating profusely, even though it was only thirty-something degrees outside. I was spotting at all the points where my clothes pressed heavily against my skin: armpits, belly button, shoulder blades, crotch. I wished I would sweat evenly, so I could change colors like a chameleon. Instead, I started to look like a leopard with a venereal disease.

As we strolled toward The Rock, I hoped the chill of winter would dry my body, and the whole time I wondered why the hell I had agreed to this. By the time I could think of an excuse to leave, we had reached the entrance. Once inside, we were greeted by two very friendly Christians handing out small programs. I could tell this was a more polished church because the paper had a nice thickness to it, and Comic Sans font was nowhere to be found.

We left the greeters and entered the main lobby. Everyone

was ridiculously nice. But I was cynical and didn't want to be there, so I assumed the folks who had greeted us were all brain-washed robots or perhaps paid actors. When you're a curmudgeon, it's hard to know how to respond to nice people, even those who might be genuine.

After a few minutes in the building, the service started. We could hear music traveling out into the lobby. My discomfort was exacerbated by a glimpse into the sanctuary. People were standing and singing. Some, I could see, had their arms outstretched. The sound pouring out was unmistakable in its simplicity, hopefulness, and lack of intricate chord progressions. I was about to walk into a room full of people belting out the chorus to an altered version of a tune that sounded familiar. We walked in just as the chorus struck: "Then sings my soul, my Savior God, to Thee…"

I bristled.

We brought Rose with us into the main worship room. Part of me was desperately hoping she'd have one of her inconsolable crying fits—probably the only time I wished for that. Oddly, even with all the lights, sounds, and strangers, she lay asleep in her carrier as heavy and still as a sack of potatoes. I did achieve one small victory; I chose a seat in the very back row, which was dark and vacant. Layla obliged.

The ceiling in the auditorium was at least thirty feet tall, and the room looked like it could seat several hundred people. It wasn't near capacity, but folks were still streaming in, finding their seats. The lights were dimmed to draw focus to the stage. On it were several musicians and a big cross (glass, of course) with interior lighting that, at present, gave it a purple hue. Above the cross were three wide projector screens. The center screen displayed a repeated loop of rolling clouds, somewhat like the computer desktop backgrounds from the early days of Microsoft. The two side screens posted digital lyrics to the songs. I wondered how long it had been since anyone had printed a hymnal.

I didn't want folks to judge me for not participating, so I parted my lips just enough to feign singing the words. I suspect a lot of people actually do this. If a professional lip reader had homed in on me, he or she would have nudged the person next to them and said, "Hey, I could be wrong, but I don't think the guy in the purple shirt wants to be here."

Shortly after 10 a.m., I noted the auditorium beginning to fill. I guess there were a lot of congregants at this place who enjoyed being fashionably late. Or perhaps they too were lip-synchers like myself who didn't want to be forced to croon in public. By the time the last song ended, I measured the room to be two-thirds full. Then a man in jeans and a black V-neck (ha, of course) walked out onto the stage and said, "Morning friends! Will you pray with me?" I had to stifle a chuckle; I really wanted him to drop the mic after his prayer.

I'm not sure what V-Neck-Guy's role was, but he wasn't the pastor. The pastor was introduced via video, where he relayed to us that he was on a mission trip, so a guest preacher would be delivering the message today. Before the substitute preacher man came out, we were asked to take a moment and greet one another.

You know, I'm a pretty social guy, but I didn't want to talk to anyone that day. As luck would have it, hardly anyone was sitting around us. I just reached over to the elderly woman in front of us who didn't react when I transferred an uncomfortable amount of sweat to her weathered hand. Then the visiting minister came out and introduced himself.

For the life of me, I can't remember the name of the man who preached. I also don't remember much about his message other than it was kind of basic and seemed to go off on tangents that were hard to tie back together. What I do remember was his catchphrase: "And that's all you need to know!" The first time he said it was maybe five minutes into the sermon, and I thought, "Well, alright, I guess we can go home now." By the fifteenth time, I was fascinated. He just kept using it as an exclamatory punch after nearly every point he made. "God will make it right. And that's all you need to know! You can find truth here. And that's all you need to know! You have a special purpose. And that's all you need to know! I ate a chimichanga today. And that's all you need to know!" (Okay, maybe not that last one.)

He finished his sermon, and then we all joined him in the penultimate prayer to summarize the highlights of his message. It reminded me of the closing statement prosecutors have to make to the jury at a felony trial. Once he had finished, V-Neck-Guy came back out and asked for the proverbial one more round of applause. Then he hit us with it. "If you want to purchase Preacher-So-and-So's new book, it's called *All You Need to Know*. It's available in softback, hardback, and audiobook formats. He'll be out in the lobby after the service, so stop by and say 'hello.'" Apparently, that was all we needed to know.

Layla despaired. She thought it was over. She was certain I would never go back to church. But she was wrong. Sheer curiosity drove me to continue a bit longer in this game. While I didn't enjoy the first experience very much, I was strangely intrigued. I mean, there were hundreds of people who congregated at The Rock, and they all heard the same thing we did. What kept them coming back? For me, the band-aid had been ripped off, so my anxiety retreated dramatically. And I knew if I pulled an "I told you so" with Layla, she'd resent me for it. Trying to raise a baby and keep balance in a marriage was hard enough. Truth be told, I needed some wins as a husband. Or at least some points.

So, we forged ahead. The Rock was a non-denominational church, so we thought maybe we'd try something else. Layla had grown up in the Episcopal Church but had branched out after college and ultimately spent most of her twenties in a Methodist Church. I had grown up in a Baptist Church, but in my twenties had branched out and spent most of my time hanging out in bars waiting for the girls from the Episcopal Church to show up. Not many did.

I tried to research other churches for us to attend. But there were so many options and not enough time to disseminate their differences. The menu of denominations and labels seemed endless. During our search, we came across: Baptist, Methodist, Presbyterian, Pentecostal, Seventh-Day Adventist, Assembly of God, Church of God, Church of Christ, United Church of Christ, Church of the Nazarene, Lutheran, Calvinist, Catholic, and on and on and on. Then there were terms like Reformed, Orthodox, Apostolic, Denominational, Non-Denominational, Independent, Fundamentalist, Salvation Army—I mean, give me a break! What's more, there seemed to be stereotypes associated with each of these segmented institutions, and from what I'd heard, half of them despised each other (or at least thought the others were going to hell). It's no wonder people are confused by Christianity.

Regardless, I kept my promise, and we ended up choosing three churches to visit over the next month or so. If I recall correctly, the mix included a Lutheran Church, a Methodist Church, and a Church of God (which I had assumed all churches were). We decided to make sure they were different shapes and sizes to see how the experiences might vary.

First on the list: the Lutheran Church. I knew the Lutherans had something to do with the friars, particularly that Martin Luther guy. Some people referred to them as "Catholic-lite." Whatever that meant.

A narrow street led to the modest church which sat at the bottom of the hill, looking stuck out of time. A stone façade flanked most of the brick structure in the kind of style hobbits from *The Lord of the Rings* might have chosen. I like hobbits, and I didn't see a purple cross made of glass, so we were good so far. It was located in a residential neighborhood, and we parked on the street, facing a small yellow bungalow-style house. Not sure why I remember the house; it just seemed to stick out.

Once inside, some of the things from our first experience carried over: friendly greeting, people singing, etc. Mostly though, this was an entirely different church. There were pews instead of chairs and hymnals instead of massive screens. It was very quaint and had an old-world feel to it.

Then I learned why it was sometimes called "Catholic-lite." The service was *long*—lots of hymns, scripture readings, creeds, and such. It felt like an hour before the sermon started. In the program they handed out, I noted an additional service listed as "contemporary." I surmised this to be a loose usage of the term. However, anything would have been better than the snooze fest we had chosen. I was bored.

I feel bad for saying that. I don't want to besmirch tradition. There are a lot of people who probably prefer a more subdued service over the flashy stuff. I'm assuming you're one of them. And I know appetites vary when it comes to God-worshiping. But it's just how I felt at the time. And I could tell I wasn't the only one; Layla was practically drooling from open-mouthed boredom.

This time Rose had a bit of a fit toward the end of the service (or what I presumed was nearing the end), so we decided to bounce out of there a few minutes early. I would've normally been extremely annoyed at having been dragged to something like this, but as we exited—for some reason—I didn't feel that way at all. If anything, my curiosity built on itself. The traditions were sort of endearing, and I appreciated the history of the place. Most of the parishioners looked about as old as the building itself. And I like old people.

Once again, folks were friendly, but in a way that seemed to respect personal space.

I reassured Layla I'd remain in the hunt with her. I still didn't think anything would come of this goose chase, but this was more interesting than cleaning the house every Sunday morning. Had I known we would encounter an exorcism I might have felt differently.

# 5

# ...the Methodists
# and the demon

I find my wife to be very peculiar. I can spend hours, or even days, trying to secure the perfect gift for a birthday or anniversary, only to get a lukewarm response followed by some comment about how I clearly wasn't listening or paying attention. Then I can go to church twice, just to appease her, and I'm rewarded with mind-blowing sex for a week. A similar response sometimes occurs if I fold the laundry, wash dishes, and vacuum all in the same day. It's like some kind of strange foreplay.

I certainly appreciate it when Layla cleans the house, but I'm not sure I've ever been aroused by it. Maybe cleaning or accompanying her to church is kind of like me doing a little pole dance for Layla. Actually, that sounds terrible. I don't fight fires or work on cell phone towers; so, I have no business being on a pole of any sort. But after getting so well rewarded for visiting the Lutheran Church, I was all-in for the next Christian adventure.

Central United Methodist Church was located at a busy

intersection by an ice cream shop called Sweet Drop, which we visited fairly often because of their killer sundaes. I loved taking Rose and watching her stick her entire face into the bowl. Something about being with her in an ice cream shop felt old fashioned. I liked that feeling. I wondered if the church would let me bring in an Oreo Cookie Fudge Ripple Drop with strawberry topping. I would argue there isn't anything more heavenly.

I read up about the Methodists before we attended. In fact, I did some cursory research on the denominations of all of the churches we visited. I was curious, and it was easy to grab quick answers via the internet, which was only a finger tap away. Speaking of that, I saw an interview with a teenager recently who was asked if he knew what an encyclopedia was. He legitimately did not know. His response was: "Do you mean Wikipedia?"

I learned the current version of the Methodist denomination, officially named the United Methodist Church, only goes back about fifty years when the Methodists merged with some other church. Of course, the original Methodist Church has been around for a couple hundred years. It was founded by a man named John Wesley. The promise of a happy wife motivated me to find out what Mr. Wesley had in store for us.

I had passed Central UMC lots of times and knew the building well. It was unmistakably church-like with its L-shaped figure, dark red brick, and tall steeple. It had a marquee sign with the service times spelled out. And sometimes there were inspirational quotes. I am grateful to digital technology for what will eventually become the eradication of those silly marquees. Growing up in the South, traveling the rural Midwest, and spending a bit of time in tiny towns in New England exposed me to a lot of these. A few years ago, I started compiling a "best of" list. Give me a second to pull this up…

Okay, so here are the ten most ridiculous statements I've ever seen written on church marquee signs:

10. Trust in God but lock your car.
9. Need a lifeguard? Ours walks on water.
8. The Easter Bunny didn't rise from the dead.
7. Forgiveness is swallowing when you'd rather spit
6. Don't give up, Moses was once a basket case.
5. Whoever is praying for snow, please stop!
4. Bring your spiritual marshmallows, our pastor is on fire!
3. Stop, drop, and roll won't work in hell.
2. We are praying for the Black family.
… and …
1. You can't enter Heaven until Jesus enters you.

Thankfully, the sign we pulled up to the day after Valentine's Day in 2015 didn't say, "God wrote the first valentine with 2 boards and 3 nails!" It just said: "Jesus loves you! Join us for worship at 10 a.m."

We got there about 9:40 because Layla despises being late for anything. In truth, it's very helpful with a small child for one of the parents to operate this way. If I were a single parent, Rose would arrive at daycare two hours late every day wearing pajamas and cowgirl boots. Thankfully, Layla makes sure both Rose and I arrive where we're supposed to be, on time, and wearing outfits that don't say: "I did the smell test before I put this on."

While I couldn't understand the need to keep the dreaded marquee, I wasn't completely put off by this church. It helped that the weather broke unexpectedly. It was a mild day for February—mid-fifties and sunny. When we walked in, we were greeted kindly and told where the infant room was located. There was a system for checking kids in and out, which I appreciated. A nice young woman was helping us input the requisite amount of information, including my fake email account, so we could tag Rose and get her settled with the other babies.

We were given an assigned number and told it would flash on the right screen of the sanctuary if there was a problem. That certainly gave us a measure of comfort. Layla and I, being first-time parents, had brought the diaper bag, medicine, toys, baby wipes, pacifier, sippy cup, Blankie, Fred the Frog, and any other possible thing we could think of that might help save our child in case of an emergency. We then left Rose, and her many accouterments, with the volunteer strangers and walked around the hallway toward the entrance to the sanctuary.

Even with the delay in dropping Rose off, we were in with plenty of time to spare. The band started playing remixed versions of old hymns, but not in a pop-rock kind of way. As we selected our seats, a pianist and guitarist were on stage by themselves, and they had a nice melody going. I felt oddly comfortable.

We stood for a few songs, and at the end, the guitarist

led us in prayer. He made me a bit queasy. I don't fault him specifically; maybe it's just the way I seem to react to public prayers accompanied by plucked guitar strings in a blatant attempt to get me to feel some sort of emotion. Luckily it was pretty short, and we sat back down.

It wasn't long before we had to stand back up again. After a brief greeting from the pastor, we were asked to say "hello" to the people around us. This time, I had to shake a few hands. Though it wasn't a massive church, I guessed there to be about 150 folks filling the room. During this greeting time, people kept saying to me, "Peace be with you."

Human behavior is interesting. Often, we just emulate those around us for fear that people will discover our fraudulent nature. I found myself saying "peace with you as well"—even though I had no idea what that meant or why I was saying it.

Once we were seated again, there were a series of announcements, traditional prayers, songs, and scriptural readings all strung in a row for about fifteen minutes. Sometimes we were asked to respond, other times just to listen. This ended abruptly after a group recitation of the Apostles' Creed. Then the children were invited to come to the altar. There the pastor gave a little lesson to the tikes as they squiggled and fidgeted around the stage. As an audience member, it reminded me of watching an elementary school play—only this play involved a man in a robe sitting on mauve-colored steps trying to impart the wisdom of the risen Christ to a bunch of five-year-olds. I'll give the guy credit for making the effort.

There was another reading, followed by the Lord's Prayer,

which I somehow mostly remembered. The congregation recited it together: "Our Father, who art in heaven, hallowed be thy name..." I again didn't want to feel out of place, and since I knew the majority of the words, I joined in this time. As I listened to myself and the crowd around me, I couldn't help but wonder what this might look like to an outsider. Say an indigenous tribal family from South America walked into the room—how would they react? Perhaps they might be thinking: *Oh no, these people are about to eat us. Run!* There's something unsettling about being surrounded by hundreds of white people chanting anything in unison.

Immediately following the Lord's Prayer, an offering was taken. I, like a lot of people, have struggled with the basket full of cash and envelopes zig-zagging through the rows of congregants. Whenever the basket lands on me, I feel like we've just played a game of hot potato, and I'm the one left holding the potato while everyone else waits for my reaction. I don't have an issue giving money to charity, or a homeless man, or my friend Brian Fetzer's "Beards and Beers 5k" GoFundMe page—but there seems to be a nefarious underbelly when it comes to the church treasury. Could be the opulent cathedrals, televangelists, and mega-church mansions. Folks like the 80s infomercial icon Peter Popoff don't help the matter either. I'd like to know how many millions he made hawking his "holy water" in the wee hours of the morning. As the kids would say these days, that guy is *creepy AF*.

Churches probably get a bad rap when it comes to taking up offerings. Like just about anything else, it takes money to get things done. I suppose this applies to saving lost souls as well. Yet, we always want churches and not-for-profit organizations to operate on shoestring budgets. The idiom essentially refers to something thin and limited, right? Maybe things would change if financial officers for charitable organizations started responding accordingly.

"How's your budget this year, Joe?"

"Well, I'd have to say it's pretty thin and limited, thanks to you."

"Ah, well, go out there and save the masses then."

I didn't leave any money in the basket. I didn't use their online giving platform either. I did, however, feel for a moment like I might be going to hell. Maybe that's why church offerings are so effective. As I was thinking this, it suddenly occurred to me that we hadn't heard a sermon yet.

I was flummoxed. Where was the main course? How did we do all that singing and praying and giving and somehow skip the requisite thirty to forty-five minutes of caution and/or encouragement from the pastor with the robe? I really wanted to see how he measured up to the "that's all you need to know" guy.

We started back in with the scriptures, singing, and praying. I was beginning to wonder if a sermon was ever going to happen. Maybe this church didn't do sermons. I was strangely okay with that. Then the music stopped, and the lead pastor climbed behind the ornate wooden podium.

"Friends, today could be the start of something new for you." As soon as he finished the sentence, we noticed the number 3107 flashing on the screen to his upper right. Layla was checking to see if it matched the sticker she was holding. I looked down to catch her scanning it from left to right with her finger: 3-1-0-7.

I've never seen someone spring from a chair so quickly. Several people probably thought she was "filled with the holy spirit." I scrambled to grab our belongings while she went to save our child.

By the time I got out of the sanctuary, Layla was gone. I could almost smell the rubber from the soles of her shoes, which had no doubt struck the ground with the quickness and ferocity of a set of racing tires. I turned the corner and saw, indeed, there was some commotion around the infant room. My heart quickened, and I picked up my pace.

As I neared the nursery where we'd handed our child over, I glanced to my right to see an open bathroom door. Inside was a woman heaving over the sink. Her hair was matted, and it looked like a can of pureed green beans had exploded onto her face and arms. She had a rather demonic appearance as she furiously tried to clean her body while trying to keep herself from throwing up. I couldn't imagine Rose doing anything to cause this kind of reaction. Then I turned the corner and caught up with Layla.

I'm going to put two words together now that I hope I never have to combine again: projectile-diarrhea.

I found Layla in a little nook near the nursery where she had retrieved our daughter. Rose surprisingly appeared quite placid, almost serene. I suppose that's the way you look after you've released a demon from your butt and cast it onto another human being. Layla and I looked at each other and knew it was time to go. We went back to the room and gathered Rose's numerous accessories. We got a sneering glare from the remaining woman who was trying to wrangle all the other children while her counterpart cleaned the shame off her body in the restroom. Layla was mortified. A thought crossed my mind: *The Lord works in mysterious ways.*

Two weeks later, true to my word, I accompanied Layla to the last church on our list. The reason I have trouble remembering the name of the church is that we didn't actually set foot inside. On our walk from the parking lot, Rose made some strange noises, and Layla panicked. She couldn't chance another demon blowout, so we got back in the car and left. And so-ended, quite unceremoniously, The Great Church Search of 2015.

My eyes feel like anvils, I should probably head out. When I come back, I'll tell you about the visit from Layla's family. They're an interesting bunch. And, somehow, they were fairly instrumental in helping God rope me back into my faith. They're also part of the reason I won't set foot in a petting zoo, ever again.

# 6

# ...animals?

I suppose it is sort of cathartic to talk through all of these experiences with you. I know it's a bit of an odd conversation to have, especially in this place. But I feel strangely okay with it, despite a few befuddled looks from the eavesdroppers.

Where did I leave off? Hmm—ah yes—the visit from Layla's family that gave me nightmares about goats. No way I can leave here without telling you that story! And it involves Linda, Garth, Rachel, and Steve. I've never said much about Layla's family, have I? Looking back, I realize they were deeply embedded in this strange faith odyssey of mine—more than I would like to admit.

In the weeks that passed after the debacle of our church visits, life resumed its rapid pace. One of my friends, a parent of three, told me that kids *make the days long, but the years short.* Doubtful he knew it was Gretchen Rubin who coined the phrase, which has become a cliché for suburban moms.

Still, I was experiencing the ongoing wisdom of that quote. Rose had started crawling and would soon be toddling around our house, getting into all sorts of mischief. She was sleeping through the night more often, and already I was struggling to recall the first few weeks of chaos and the 2 a.m. swaddling that occurred after we brought her home from the hospital. I began to savor every moment since we still hadn't decided if kid number two was an option. Each time Rose sputtered, "Da-da," I thought it might be the last time I'd ever be called by that name.

Layla was back in full swing as well, and we resumed our march to the beat of the modern dual-working family household. Work was busy. She kept the executives organized, and I tried to close deals. Things seemed to be going well.

Yet I couldn't help but feel the quiet tension that existed in our little world. Don't get me wrong—Layla was every bit the fiery, but doting wife she'd always been. Still, a far-off sadness pervaded her demeanor sometimes. The listless routine amplified the uncertainty of her spiritual convictions as we resumed the distractions of life. I'm sure I didn't help with my implied indifference, which might've been received as satisfaction with our failure to land a church.

But secretly, something had sprung up inside of me. You would think I felt exalted by the epic bomb that was our church search. But nothing could be further from the truth. I'm not sure why, but my brain started to swirl. There were philosophical questions at every turn. Was life more than a means to an end? Was there really something greater than just what we experience in our brevity on earth? Was I supposed to just work, provide for my family, eventually retire, take vacations, and then die?

I plunged into a pre-mid-life crisis. Maybe I needed to buy a motorcycle. Maybe I needed to take a month off and hike part of the Appalachian Trail—or ride a motorcycle down the Appalachian Trail. I was fairly certain that motorcycles could outrun bears, even at top galloping speeds.

But age and responsibility often betray whimsy and fearlessness. When I was younger, I could jump out of an airplane, skinny dip in January, or try to break a 6-minute mile after gorging at an all-you-can-eat pizza buffet without any thought whatsoever to the potential consequences. I suppose, as I've gotten older, I tend to rely less on luck to survive and more on rational choices, which is why the spiritual invasion was messing with me. At the time, I didn't find much rationality in it.

My head rattled during the last weeks of an extended winter that year. I had a few near-sleepless nights pondering the meaning of life. I took deep dives into the internet, which is where one finds the most rational thoughts on the meaning of life. A couple of churches ran Google Ads purporting to have the answers, but then so did Stanford University with its exposé on Plato. There was a YouTube video called "The Meaning of Life in Under 60 Seconds." And, of course, I explored the Wikipedia galaxy. "Conceptions of morality" eventually led me to the "Roman Empire," which eventually led me to the official Wikipedia page for the movie *Rocky IV*.

Is it odd that I found *Rocky IV* to be more philosophically moving than all the other pages?

I couldn't completely pinpoint my restlessness. Sure, some of it I could attribute to my reacquaintance with God in his myriad churches. And yes, I wanted to feel more complete, more connected in my marriage. But likely, I was agitated because the solid, cynical wall I'd built was beginning to fracture under its own weight. My life's construction felt fragmentary, inadequate. I began thinking about what exactly I was contributing to the world.

Cold temperatures, with their suppressing, shut-in qualities, presented a lot of opportunities to deliberate. But Spring was coming and, as the season inherently might imply, action was stirring. Dead leaves were quickly disappearing from the ground with new ones sprouting on naked branches. Frost was giving way to dew and clothing was becoming less layered. Animals and insects scampered about more visibly. In a few short weeks, Layla's sister and her family would be spending the weekend with us again. It was almost Easter.

Layla's dad is a huge Eric Clapton fan. The two girls, Layla and Linda, are named after two of his favorite Clapton songs. I'm not sure how Layla's mom let him get away with the name choices, but it's one of the few battles he seems to have won.

Layla's sister Linda lives about three hours south of us in a mid-sized town that used to be a bustling port city for railroad and river workers. A lot of towns fit that category, or something like it, these days. Old economic forces like factories, farms, and freight—which laid these towns' very foundations—are no longer the same industries they used to be. You can see remnants of the past in the downtown area where they live. A decaying newspaper factory, a stockyard, and a rail depot have either been reworked or put out to pasture.

Linda and her husband, Garth, sometimes struggle to make ends meet since good jobs are scarce and competitive. They live in a modest two-bedroom house. They don't take vacations often, and Garth has a second part-time job. But they still seem to make it work after eleven years of marriage.

As with most extended families who don't live in the same city, there are requisite gatherings that take place each year. Compromises around the main holidays vary, and then—of course—weddings, birthdays, and other events bring people together. Though we'd just hosted Christmas for both sides of the family, it was agreed that Layla's family would be back in town for Easter. The holiday celebrating the death and resurrection of Jesus was important to her parents. It also happened to fall close to the birthday of Mario and Drew—Garth and Linda's twin boys. The boys were about to turn six.

Garth, a child of the 80s, never relinquished his obsession with the Super Mario Bros. He lobbied hard to name his first-born (by seventeen minutes) after the video game plumber with the red hat and the unmistakable mustache. I always love it when people ask, "Is that a family name?" Mario was also the more advanced of the two twins in almost every way. The thing Drew was most known for was his obsession with his little penis. He was renowned in the Davis household for running up to Linda and shaking it at her without warning.

# THE CHURCH WORKER

I really like Linda, Garth, and their kids. They're what I'd call "light-blue collar"—educated people who also shoot guns and shop at Dollar General. They don't have a propensity for bullshit, and they're pretty passionate about their opinions. We've had some good conversations. Layla's parents, however, are another matter.

Like a lot of people, Layla and I both have a tenuous relationship with our in-laws. It's not necessarily anything they've done wrong, but marriage essentially forces relatives into relationships they probably would never have developed on their own. The level of tension depends on proximity, the number of grandchildren, and the general flexibility of the humans involved as agendas collide.

I'm reminded of zoologists who experiment with animal pairings. Sure, sometimes it works out. I read about the story of Shere Khan, Baloo, and Leo—who were rescued by Noah's Ark Animal Sanctuary in Atlanta. It's not every day that a black bear, a Bengal tiger, and a lion become best friends—although the story neglected to include any descriptions of conflict (like the tiger and the lion making subtle comments about the black bear's weight).

Layla's mom, Rachel, would pull out her claws a time or two, mostly to fight with Linda. Linda's aggravation would eventually collect and reform into the snarling and gnashing of teeth at Garth. And Steve, Layla's dad, would be desperately searching for a dark cave in which to hide until the weekend was over. In preparation, I ate most of our groceries, depleted my car's gas tank, threw away all but two rolls of toilet paper, and neglected to replenish our diaper supply for Rose. I needed multiple excuses to extricate myself throughout the weekend. Solo errands are like mini-vacations from family.

We had a plan for the weekend that included dinner Friday night, zoo on Saturday, and then brunch/church on Sunday, which was a bit of a conundrum for me. Layla's family members were all devout Christians with congregations of their own. Rachel and Steve still attended the same Episcopal church where Layla grew up, while Garth and Linda had found a non-denominational church where they could support women's rights while also suggesting death by firing squad as an effective means of capital punishment.

Garth and Linda arrived later than expected, so we canceled the dinner and instead ordered Chinese takeout. We did the usual catching up, and then everyone went to bed early. The next day was the birthday celebration for the twins. Plus, it would be Rose's first visit to the zoo. Based on what happened—it should've been her last.

We woke up the next day, and I did my breakfast thing, cooking mountainous heaps of eggs, bacon, and toast. I garnished it with fruit, which I felt helped offset the bacon. We knew what was in store: a brisk day filled with ornery children who didn't have the social maturity to appreciate the privilege they were experiencing. We left the house around nine to try and beat the crowd. Everyone else in the city had the same idea.

It was indeed a chilly April day. The forecast didn't call for rain, and yet clouds decided to spit cold droplets consistently throughout the morning. Aside from that, I was genuinely excited to introduce Rose to the zoo. We had a special little outdoor pavilion reserved for Mario and Drew so we could celebrate their birthdays. It was located right next to the petting zoo.

Rose was having a particularly good morning, which meant—despite the weather—so were we. The grandparents hadn't overshared their opinions on parenting. Garth and Linda weren't fighting. Drew had yet to take his penis out of its holster. I considered the day a win already.

We paid the $10 to park and then followed the flock of zoo-goers down the concrete bridge that connected the parking lot to the entrance. Once inside, we noted families, scurrying about in every state of joy and sadness. Some kids seemed elated to be amongst live animals in a controlled environment. Others were super pissed that their mommy didn't buy them an ice cream cone at ten in the morning. There's not a lot of camaraderie at zoos or theme parks. I'm guessing the most commonly uttered phrase is, "What are all of these people doing here?"

We sifted our way through the crowd to find our birthday pavilion. As it turns out, it was more of a birthday umbrella, but it was enough to fit our group. The twins immediately noticed the autonomous red metal dispensers that were the source of the animals' food. People were pumping quarters into these machines, which churned out handfuls of small brown pellets.

At most petting zoos, there are numerous ways to spend

money. You can buy food, milk, photos, etc. We purchased a bottle of milk for both of the boys so they could feed the baby goats. I plunked in two quarters so Rose and I could feed the other animals. The fenced enclosures held ducks, goats, chickens, pigs, and in a separate section, there were a couple of ponies.

Rose was unbelievably adorable. I mean it. There have been so many moments when I relished being a dad, and this was one of them. She giggled hysterically every time an animal came up to us. I was so enthralled that I wasn't aware of anything else going on around us. Only when I heard the screams did I look up.

Not ten feet away from Drew and Mario, a little boy was being dragged by his arm across the enclosure. Plumes of dirt materialized right and left, and audible gasps were coming from the onlookers. As the dust cleared, I caught a clearer view of what was happening. One of the large adult goats had somehow gotten into the enclosure. The goat's mouth was clasped deep over the nipple of a milk bottle, partially devouring the tiny fingers of the boy who held the bottle. The yanking and thrashing seemed out of character for a farm animal. Parents were losing their minds.

The goat clamped down and pulled the child violently, not willing to release the child's arm, which reflexively clung to the plastic bottle. In some ways, I empathized with the goat. He had been stuck in that adult pen for far too long. I guess he got tired of watching the kid goats eat candy and ice cream all day while he ate lentils and quinoa. Every goat has its breaking point.

The animal continued wrenching until I saw a man run over and start screaming and swinging at it. It's weird to say, but I'm pretty sure the man—clearly the father of the boy with his arm in the goat's mouth—slapped the goat in the face. It wasn't a punch, and it wasn't a grab. He definitely smacked that goat.

The goat pulled away and ran to a far corner of the pen. I strained to see what it was doing and noticed that it had won. The bottle of milk was in its mouth, and it was sucking joyfully. I was impressed. But then I heard wailing behind me. I turned back to the man who was attending to his son. I was close enough to see it. The goat had partially severed the boy's right index finger; it was hanging loosely off the bone. The man scooped his son up and ran for the exit. I couldn't imagine what he was going to tell the doctor when asked about the origin of the injury.

At that point, I was done with zoo animals. I mean—if a goat can bite off your finger, what can an African lion do? We kept it together long enough to celebrate the birthdays, though we were unsure just how much the trauma had translated to our kids. Mario was balling up napkins and playing wastepaper basketball. Drew kept grabbing at his crotch. Rose was throwing cake on the ground in hopes that an animal might come over. God bless the resiliency of children.

Since our kids didn't seem to be displaying any visible anguish, we continued on our merry way, letting them explore the rest of the park. It reminded me of what happens when you pass a horrendous car accident. You slow down for a moment, lament the situation with phrases like "I hope no one died" ... then you continue on with your day. We weren't going to let one little incident involving someone else's child having his finger gnawed by a farm animal ruin the rest of our day, now were we? We had more in common with those zoo animals than we probably would have liked to admit.

After the zoo, we took the whole family out to Jurassic Pizza, home of the T-Rex—a 36" pizza that is free if two people can finish it in under an hour. There were nine of us, and we ate maybe half of it. We boxed the rest and headed home. That night I had a dream about zombie goats covered in pizza that had pale, child-sized fingers instead of hooves.

The next day was Easter Sunday. What I know about Easter is that it's supposed to celebrate Jesus' rising from the dead. A lot is riding on that claim. If it isn't true, then the whole religion basically collapses on itself. Yet somehow, we've managed to make it about a *Lord of the Flies* version of a treasure hunt where tiny toddlers trample each other to retrieve plastic eggs filled with jelly beans and marshmallow chickens.

Layla's parents insisted on going to church Easter Sunday, but I didn't have it in me after the goat episode. So, I stayed home with Rose while everyone else went to the church service at The Rock. Layla couldn't think of anywhere else to take them. I wasn't there, but apparently, the service was *inspiring*, and Layla's family asked why we weren't regulars at the church. Also, Rachel wanted to know if her son-in-law would ever have a relationship with Christ Jesus. I doubt mothers-in-law have much success with evangelism, especially when they throw around phrases like "Christ Jesus."

I joined everyone for Easter brunch, which Garth noted was "a meal reserved for privileged people." At the time he made the statement, there was a noticeable ketchup stain on his shirt and a substantial hole on the left leg of his jeans. Again, I really like that guy. Layla quietly told me that The Rock had been much better, but still not what we were looking for. Garth and Linda seemed eager to get the check and hit the road. Rachel was proselytizing, and I was sure Steve wanted to shut himself in a dark room with Pink Floyd playing on repeat. The bill came, and Steve insisted on paying it. We all reached for our credit cards in a pretend effort to fund our portion of the meal. Then we all feigned our sincere goodbyes and went our separate ways.

What was left at our house was the cleaning of countertops, the washing of dishes, the changing of sheets, the disposing of trash, and all the other chores that happen after you've hosted a group of overnight guests. Layla and I put things back together and crashed into bed not long after dinner.

The next morning, we resumed our regular tempo, albeit with a bit less drama than we had experienced the preceding days. I'm sure I was lamenting the visit from Layla's family to some degree. Although, to be honest, I had felt a bit guilty for not joining the family for church on Easter. Maybe I was still reeling from our recent church shopping experiences.

Or perhaps I was trying to avoid the questions of life and faith that had crept into my head.

Sometimes, however, there are life events that are so devastating you don't know where to turn. People enter houses of worship as part of their desperate search for answers. I just never thought I'd be one of those people.

# 7

# diagnosis...

On April 22nd, a day before my 34th birthday, Steve phoned to tell us that Rachel had been diagnosed with stage three breast cancer. Layla was devastated. She was certain she was going to lose her mother. Rachel, the person she called on the way home from work every day. The person she confided in when times were difficult. The flawed, but caring matriarch who brought Layla into this world, and blanketed her with comfort the way only a mother can. I watched, listened, and tried to support as best I could.

Since it's just the two of us here right now, I'm going to be honest with you. I loved Layla, but I was somewhat indifferent about Rachel. Layla shared a life with me. We had adventures. We laughed together. We lived together. We confided in one another. We had sex. We reveled in the joys of parenting. I could go on, but the point is that there were plenty of reasons for me to be invested in grief for Layla.

Rachel I'd only known for a few short years, most of which were incentivized by formality dinners, family gatherings, or the providing of respite for Layla and me by taking care of Rose for a day or two. How much can you really know someone when that's the basis of your relationship? It was like when Uncle Greg died. Rick and I attended the funeral out of respect for Mom, and we cried when she cried. But we didn't cry for Greg. We didn't really know him.

I began thinking of Rachel's terminal situation and how I would respond to her passing, if it came to that. I would have a general human sadness, of course. But I wondered if my emotions would display real pain or loss. Then I thought of Rose. Even though she was still very young, Rose certainly was benefitting from the love of people who were so devoted to her. This included Rachel who, outside of Layla and me, might have been the most devoted. I had a new perspective. I might not see eye to eye with my mother-in-law all the time, but if not for her, most of the things I truly care about in life wouldn't exist.

Like many people with a cancer diagnosis, Rachel did not want to be treated like an invalid. She had fire just like Layla and was stubborn in a way that was both heroic and frustrating. The sighs and pensive, far-off looks revealed Rachel's inner fear, but she masked this with a determination that I've typically only seen in people who are battling life in ways most of us can't even fathom. She also found a sense of humor, though she probably didn't realize it. The funniest things I heard Layla's mom say while she was being tested for cancer treatments were:

"If I have to shave my head, at least I'll match your father."

"Yes, doctor, I exercise. I do ten pushups every day."

"My boobs were starting to sag anyway, so can I get some new ones?"

"If you miss my vein again, I'm going to stab you with that thing."

Layla prayed for her mom intensely every night. Sometimes the words would be audible, the intensity igniting her voice box while her eyes were still closed. I was, all at once, envious and incredulous. Envious in that I had never believed in something so strongly that I cried out for relief. Incredulous in that a good part of me believed those prayers were wasted because no one other than me was listening.

In the background of all of this, our city had fully awakened from its winter slumber. Rains had breathed life into the ground, and things grew. Playgrounds sprang to life, runners gave their soles to the streets once again, and the daylight extended thanks to the regulatory adjustment of our clocks. The blossoming season was a stark contrast to the bleak, suffocating diagnosis of cancer.

One Sunday evening in early May, Layla and I headed home after a visit with her parents. Rachel had not looked well. Terms like *metastasis*, *malignant*, *biopsy*, and *bone marrow* were being tossed around with monotonous delivery, almost as if they were mathematical certainties. It was difficult to keep up the rosy charade of hope. I could tell the weight of the diagnosis was beginning to crush Layla.

During the car ride, Layla said, "I'm not sure I'm ready for this."

I assumed "this" meant losing her mother.

"I know, babe. Is there anything I can do to help?"

"Actually, there is. I wonder if you'd pray for her tonight?"

I wanted to say yes, but I didn't know how to pray anymore. As I pondered an answer, I noticed a brick monument up ahead with a sign illuminated in blue letters. It read, "Turning Point." As we drove past, I saw that the sign was announcing a church. I squinted to make out a tall, slender building with a few panes of stained glass and a generally unassuming appearance. I didn't see any traditional Christian symbols, but the way the building came to a point at the top and the shape of the windows gave it away. Though it was dusk, the lights were on, and the front doors were open with people trickling in—which meant they were having a service or a very oddly-timed wedding. Our car seemed to make a U-turn by itself.

I once looked up the phrase "divine intervention" in the *Urban Dictionary*. It said: "When the hand of God comes down from heaven to stop motherfuckin' bullets." I assume Samuel L. Jackson submitted that entry. At any rate, I've struggled with the concept of divine intervention my entire life. A few near-death experiences and some witnessed medical miracles will mess with your head. But there were also folks for whom an act of God included the landing of a primo parking space at Target, at which point they utter "thank you, Lord." Were the hands of God moving the wheel of my car hard left to make a 180-degree turn? Or was I making a conscious decision to seek help because I felt so inept at assuaging my wife's grief over her mother's misery? Hard to say.

Regardless, the result was the same. I found myself pulling into the parking lot of a church at 6 p.m. on Sunday, May 10th, 2015. This was different than any of the other experiences I'd had visiting churches with Layla. I wasn't wondering about the layout of the service, the style of preaching, or the music. I didn't even see what denomination presided over this particular church. I was simply desperate.

Nary a word passed between Layla and me. She knew I was reaching for anything that could provide her the solace and comfort that I could not at that moment. We unbuckled Rose from the car seat and strode across the pavement toward the sidewalk that led to the building. It was a gusty evening, and the wind made conversation a bit untenable, which I found to be a relief. We walked in silence until we reached the steps, at which point we were greeted by a friendly volunteer who handed us a small pamphlet. She said, "Welcome, it's good to see you." It looked as though Layla was about to break down and cry upon hearing that simple nicety.

My memories related to the first visit to Turning Point are blurry. I wasn't paying close attention like I had been during our visits to the other houses of worship earlier in the year. I mean, now I can tell you a lot about the building: the architecture, the rooms, the pastor, the toilet that doesn't flush if you have a heavy bowel movement. But on this occasion, my senses were dulled and vulnerable. It felt warm when we crossed the threshold into the sanctuary, and a piano player feathered out the final notes of a song. We plopped down in the back row and kept Rose bundled up in her tiny blue blanket. Layla handed Rose over to me, and I cradled her as the music tapered off. A youngish man walked out onto the platform and began to pray.

There are two things I remember vividly from my first experience at Turning Point. One was the sermon, and the other was a phrase stated as part of the opening prayer, something I heard less than five minutes after sitting down. Midway through his prayer, the guy on the stage said, "Some of you sitting in this room are wrestling with some very hard things. You may not even know why you came here tonight." The hair on my neck stood up involuntarily.

Unlike some of the other churches we'd visited, this church got to the meat and potatoes quickly. There was a short testimonial video after the prayer, but then a pastor came out and started right into his message. Turning Point packages their sermons as part of a series, and this one was called "Good Grief." I loathed the moniker, but I absorbed the message like a sponge. The words hit a little too close to home. I had chosen this church on a whim after a long day of watching Layla grieve at a hospital. Thus, I'll admit, I was a bit unnerved by the preaching about grief. However, the pastor was really, really good. I hadn't heard preaching done the way he performed it. His oratory was genuine yet fallible, humor with gravitas, challenging, but simplistic.

The one word I wouldn't use to describe the first sermon I ever heard from Pastor Jake is "uplifting." I find this odd because a lot of successful preachers tend to have uplifting messages. That's why so many people go to church—to soak up some hopeful words, which might help them make sense of the otherwise crappy situations that occur in their lives. Well, that or to find out who is or isn't going to hell.

Such was not the case this particular Sunday evening. It was raw and pragmatic. The pastor used real-life examples combined with the scriptures to illustrate his points. One of the stories was about a woman suffering from cancer. If I had to sum up the entirety of the church service in one word, I'd say it was "comforting."

Layla cried three times but left the place looking slightly less burdened. During the message and throughout the worship experience, she squeezed my hand firmly and leaned onto my shoulder so that my shirt could dry her tears. It was a powerful event, one that I couldn't brush off with my usual quippy remarks. And Rose never interrupted with a single cry; or poop.

As we walked back to the parking lot, Layla called Steve. "Dad," she said, "I think everything's gonna be okay." They shared a few more words and then hung up. Driving home, Layla leaned over and kissed me on the cheek. "Thank you," she said. We both knew she'd found her church, and that we would be coming back. My body autopiloted our car home while my brain swirled like the haze of headlights bouncing off our vehicle. I wasn't comfortable with the idea of pledging my allegiance to a church, but I was open to anything that helped get my wife through this trauma. And maybe, just maybe, God really did reach down and stop motherfuckin' bullets.

# 8

# Turning Point

Sometimes I feel like I've been running from God my whole life. I rejected him when I was younger as people tried to beat me over the head with the Bible. I mean that quite literally. An older woman teaching Sunday school once hit me over the head with the *New King James Version*, which consequently is pretty dense. Her metaphorical beatdown was even worse.

Later in high school, I went to my friend's youth group from time to time, primarily because there was a girl who I really wanted to kiss. As it turned out, I had no idea how to kiss, and so—of course—I partially blamed God for her rejection. Then in college, I got into Universalism because that's what you do when you drink a lot and think you know everything. But I never committed fully to the God of the Bible. I had too many questions with no answers. Too many smart friends with great arguments about socialization and evolution. And probably too many experiences of judgment rather than acceptance.

And yet here I was, sitting amongst the Christians again, feeling completely out of place. Layla and I began to attend Turning Point regularly. She was beaming again, and I certainly appreciated that. I, on the other hand, was somewhere between cautious, curious, and churlish. Pastor Jake kept me from stepping off the cliff.

What made his talks so appealing was that they felt less like sermons and more like master classes in religious theory and pragmatism. He rarely sugar-coated, but rarely got too heavy-handed. Always there was a challenge to seek knowledge, question inherent biases, and be open to the opinions of others. History lessons were given to provide context, and he would often say that it was indeed difficult to practice religion with any fervency, flawed as we all are. And, best of all, he wasn't boring.

My transition was a plodding, dubious affair. I still thought there might be a chance Pastor Jake would ask us all to drink some blue Kool-Aid one Sunday so we could reach the extraterrestrial spaceship chasing down the Hale-Bopp comet. I can't believe that's an actual thing that happened to those Heaven's Gate people, by the way. Layla, in contrast, was full throttle. After we'd only been going to Turning Point for a few weeks, she started to bug me about volunteering. It probably had something to do with the fact that her mom's health had taken a turn for the better, and that I had finally succumbed to her wishes.

Around the time Layla was probing me to become more involved at Turning Point, I picked up a Bible for the first time in a long time. I didn't have a plan or anything. I just flipped from chapter to chapter one day, perusing whatever passage opened up as I absently thumbed the pages. I stumbled into the book of Deuteronomy, landing on Chapter 25. I gave it a pedestrian glance and was about to turn the page when somehow my eyes caught verses 11-12. "[11]If two men are fighting, and the wife of one man tries to rescue her husband by grabbing the other man's private parts, [12] you must cut off her hand. Don't have any mercy."

Yeah, I was going to need some clarification on stuff like that before jumping right in and volunteering at church. Also, if I decided to become a biblical literalist, I'd probably need to cut off Layla's hand based on an incident that happened at a bar in 2012.

While I continued to wrestle with ancient texts and personal demons, Layla took the next step. She joined the team that many churches call "Connections" or "First Impressions." At the time, I thought it meant she stood outside and smiled at people while handing out worship programs. It seemed like the easiest volunteer job I'd ever heard of, and I wasn't sure why she had to arrive an hour early every time she served. Apparently, there was a lot of behind-the-scenes stuff to help with, but I was usually too busy tending to Rose to get into the details. Soon enough, I would find out more than I ever wanted to know about the Turning Point Connections Team.

I got to know more about our new church every week,

discovering its DNA. Turning Point is what is known as a "multi-site church." When we first started attending, there were two locations about thirty minutes from each other. Sometimes we'd be subjected to video sermons since Pastor Jake preached most of the messages and couldn't be in both places at once. I suppose there wasn't a gifted enough doppelganger to pull off live preaching 100 percent of the time. At first, I loathed this setup. I could tell when it was a video Sunday because a big projector screen would be dangling from the ceiling above the musicians on the stage. After a while, I got used to it. We spend so much time looking at screens anyway; it wasn't that difficult to assimilate.

I discovered that Turning Point was a fairly open-minded church. Some of this was from the pulpit, although typically, Pastor Jake was good about toeing the line. And passing references to the hunting, farming, and football of his youth led me to believe the pastor held onto a few core conservative values. But nothing in his messages felt truly political or divisive. The preaching was simply meant for human beings struggling with faith. I fit that category, as did so many of what I discerned to be an island of misfits and outcasts attending the church.

For starters, there were quite a few people from the LGBTQ community. This surprised me since, according to the church I'd known growing up, those folks had a decent chance of bursting into flames the moment they set foot into the sanctuary. Also, there seemed to be at least some racial and ethnic diversity at Turning Point—mostly Asian and African-American. Don't get me wrong; there was a lot of vanilla. But it was nice to see that the appeal of the message crossed cultural lines and brought people together, even if I didn't think it was necessarily changing the world.

I began to appreciate the Turning Point vibe. Although I still wasn't comfortable talking to people about Jesus. When I did, I'd usually pretend to be well-versed and offer advice. I'm not sure why; maybe in the back of my mind, I felt I'd be judged if I didn't sound like a smart Christian when talking to the other Christians. Sadly, I'm pretty good at this. People frequently think I know more about stuff than I actually do. Or maybe they think I'm full of shit and just don't tell me so that we can keep up normal affectations.

By the summer of 2015, we were regulars at Turning Point Church. My wife was, unsurprising to me, a "rising star" volunteer. Rose was embracing the children's ministry, as much as an infant can. And I was learning how to be a Christian all over again.

Sometimes I would strike up short conversations with congregants, inquiring about their reactions to the sermons. Subconsciously, I set traps, waiting for the inevitable criticism that would finally prove that these folks were no different than those I encountered as an impressionable nine-year-old. But I was never corrected or judged for butchering interpretations or displaying a laughable lack of spiritual knowledge. In fact, I was fascinated by the mutually shared shallow biblical acumen during many of my encounters.

This particular church seemed to have a lot of people in it who claimed that they didn't know the Bible as well as they wished they did. I found that unbelievably refreshing. I began to see that a good percentage of these Sunday attendees were struggling with faith. They were the formerly jaded Christians, the unwelcomed, and the unchurched. I slowly started to let go of the idea that I should be a spiritual intellectual in the "prerequisite" understandings of the Bible. I started to embrace the fact that, I too, was just another dummy trying to figure out life and faith. It was quite liberating.

An interaction with Layla one Sunday in late June pulled the linchpin from my already deteriorating skepticism. She was chatting with two middle-aged women who had just started attending the church. I had scooped up Rose from the nursery and was cooing with her playfully while eavesdropping on the conversation. Layla's voice caught me first. "Wow. I don't even know what to say. Is there anything I can do to help?"

"No, just pray for us, I guess. We had pretty much given up on church and only came here on a whim. The message today really hit home for us. It's what we needed."

"I'm glad to hear that," Layla said. "My husband and I only started coming here a little while ago. That's him over there with our daughter. We definitely have been through some challenges this year as well. I can tell you that being able to lean on this church has been a game-changer. I can only hope it will be the same for you."

"Let's hope so. It's been a really rough year."

Rose was squiggling, and my attention was drawn away for a few moments. By the time I checked back, the couple was gone. Layla finished up her volunteer duties while Rose and I bounced around at the back of the sanctuary. Then we all headed out to the car together. On the drive home, I probed her a bit on the conversation I'd overheard. "So, I caught part of that talk you were having with the two ladies there. What was that about?"

"Oh my God, Joe, it was heart-wrenching. They both lost their moms in the last two months. And neither of their dads have ever accepted that they are gay, despite them both growing up in the church."

"How'd you leave it?"

"I just told them I'd pray for them. What else could I say? I'm not sure it was that helpful."

"No, babe. I think you're right. With something that heavy, they probably just needed some relief, a sense that someone or something will help get them through it. It's how I felt when you told me about your mom's cancer diagnosis, and I didn't know what the hell to do."

After I said this, it struck me that people carry a lot of baggage into church, often without anyone ever knowing. Of course, some just go because it's the faith tradition that raised them; they have a sense of duty or familiarity. But others, like the couple my wife tried to console, have a complex tapestry of life issues. They're trying to discern whether God is real and if so, is he listening, and can anyone help them make sense of it all.

The scientist in my brain has never ceased grappling with the idea of a divine being creating everything in this world and beyond. This creator has supposedly conscripted an inspired, dense, and contextualized book from which we were all intended to understand its meaning, either for ourselves or through interpreters like Pastor Jake. Again, for a fairly logical person, this has stretched the limits of my completely average consciousness.

But I was being reminded of the positive power of this book, and the subsequent communities that sprang up to share its message. I had to ask myself some tough questions. Would I spend all my time studying the veracity of the Bible? If so, I'd probably miss the poignant turns of phrase from Pastor Jake as he drove home logical points that might apply to my life. Would I remain secretly snarky about the naiveté of Christians? If so, I'd never fully embrace Layla, who now was thriving in a way I had never seen in all our years together. I needed a way to unpack all of this.

Then I looked down at Rose. She was about to celebrate her first birthday. Maybe exposing her to church wasn't the worst idea in the world. I still wanted her to grow up with a discerning demeanor and an inquiring mind, but if there was truth and healing to be found in God, I wanted her to have it.

When we got home, I walked into the kitchen, closed my eyes, placed my hands on the smooth gray countertop, and silently muttered a prayer. "God, please guide Layla toward planning a sensible birthday party for our daughter, and not one of those over-the-top themed blowouts that Rose won't remember anyway."

Maybe not the most heartfelt prayer ever lifted up. You

ever tried talking to God? It feels weird. I eventually made peace with being below average in the prayer department. And, as I would learn many times over, not all prayers are answered.

# 9

# the first birthday...

Have I told you how much I despise almost everything about one-year-old birthday parties? Layla and I had agreed we wouldn't follow the crowd with its smash cakes and superfluous soirees themed for tiny people who weren't making memories. We had made a lot of pre-child promises in the months leading up to Rose's birth. Here are a few that were quickly demolished in Rose's first year:

1. Our child will only eat health foods like carrots and avocados. She will not eat chicken nuggets or mac 'n cheese.
2. Screen time will be limited to thirty minutes per day and filled primarily with brain-building programs like *Sesame Street* and Neil DeGrasse Tyson.
3. She will sleep in her own bed or crib after three months, and we will resume our sex goal of four times per week.

4. Rose will feed primarily from Layla's teat for the first six months.
5. We will not consult the internet every time our child coughs.
6. We will not get one of those creepy baby monitor cameras that makes our child look like a character from a horror film.
7. Absolutely no ridiculous, over-the-top first birthday party!

Yes, we broke all of them—some in hilarious ways. For instance, three weeks after Rose came home from the hospital, Layla gave up on the breast pump machine. It sounded like a broken air conditioner and produced such a dearth of milk that even a tiny kitten would've looked up and said, "You've got some stingy teats lady." Shortly after Layla quit breastfeeding, I was rocking Rose during a late-night shift while watching the fourth season of *Breaking Bad* on Netflix. I wasn't wearing a shirt. She was just close enough to clamp her small lips around my hairy nipple and give it quite the mouth tug. Much to her chagrin, and my elation, nothing came out.

Most parents will tell you they don't remember a lot from the first year. I think that's why there are siblings in this world. But a lot of folks do have some inkling of memory from their child's first birthday. Let me tell you what I think the first birthday party should be for first-time parents—it should be a big celebration involving friends and family. Someone can come up with a cheesy theme, and all the kids should be invited. There should be cake, cupcakes, cookies, and every other confection that can be drenched in sugar. While the children run amok in an over-sweetened rage, the birthday girl's parents should be out getting hammered and consuming the fine foods they haven't been able to enjoy since it became a habit to eat fast while standing up. The friends and family should buy them a hotel room, and then someone should volunteer to stay until at least mid-afternoon the next day. The parents should be allowed to sleep off any debauchery that they deservedly had the previous evening. After grandma puts the child down for an afternoon nap, the parents return home and become parents again. Because no one ever honors the fact that two capricious, loosely responsible adults managed to keep a tiny infant alive for an entire year. That's something to celebrate!

We'll file that away under *pipe dream* and move on.

Instead, here we were on July 6th, 2015, announcing that our child had survived a full year in spite of her parents' lack of knowledge, expertise, or intuition. In front of our house was a yellow brick road. I wish I could say it was intentionally purposed to be there by the city street department. But no, this was just one component of the elaborate *Wizard of Oz* theme that Layla had concocted for our twenty-pound infant.

To be fair to Layla, the theme was not originally born out of a love for *The Wizard of Oz* movie. She happens to have a deep appreciation for the song "Somewhere Over the Rainbow" as performed by the late Israel Kamakawiwo'ole. Yeah, I'm sure I butchered that last name, but you've probably never heard of him anyway. I give Layla a ton of props for her admiration of the song—it is a good one. I just don't see why I couldn't have played it on the guitar, offered Rose a cupcake and a candle, and then sent her off to an early nap. That would have been glorious.

However, let me say this: Layla is a very cool chick. You've seen some of this in person, although your interactions have been regrettably brief. She has a way of engaging with people that makes them feel heard and valued. And she has a keen eye for style, music, and the arts. Yet, she is prone—like many mothers—to preposterous gestures in the name of her child.

I've learned over the years to embrace the goofy—and sometimes annoying—motherhood whims. Probably because I spout out enough dad jokes to make Laffy Taffy writers blush. And partly because it's one of the ways Layla expresses her love. And it's a grandiose kind of love, the kind that not all parents provide, unfortunately. So, because of that, I found myself on a summer Sunday in July wearing a full-piece, head-to-toe, polyester Cowardly Lion costume. To be fully transparent with you, which is easy to do, I had consumed two high-octane local craft IPAs before donning the suit. Hey, everybody wins.

The party went off without a hitch.

Okay, I'm lying. Half of the food was left untouched. Our single friend Ashley pounded the "Wicked Witch Margaritas" and passed out on the toddler bed. Rose cried at least half the time. And the miniature inflatable ball pit that Layla's sister had purchased at Walmart exploded when Drew decided to tap into his WWE persona. But you know what? Nobody died. This included Rachel, whose body had recently responded so well to treatment that she had the energy to softly chastise a few of the youngsters at the party. I was considered one of the "youngsters."

For birthdays this snazzy, you have to wake up early to set up, and there's no second shift custodial crew to help you clean up the whole damned mess afterward. It was exhausting. But then, so is raising a child. And for that matter, so is loving someone. With all the activity, Rose went down without a fight early in the afternoon. I unsheathed my sweaty lion costume and helped Layla restore order to the home. As we were cleaning up, Layla said, "Hey, do you want to go to church tonight?"

Almost subconsciously, I began walking toward the kitchen with the intention of stabbing my wife with a plastic fork covered in green frosting. Church? Only an hour earlier, a kindergartener had smacked me in the testicles with a Doc McStuffins doll. That toy carries plastic medical equipment; it's not all plush. I just wanted to lie down and recover. The flurry of hurried activity had taken its toll. Church was the last thing on my mind.

I momentarily recalled seasons of my life being filled with lazy Saturdays and Sundays. Few and far between were those kinds of days now. Weekends were a sprint, not even the "Lord's Day" was protected anymore. All the youth sports were active, big box stores were open twenty-four hours, and every one of my neighbors was out mowing their grass if the weather permitted. I even passed a strip club driving back from Texas last year that was advertising a Sunday surf-n-turf buffet. I wasn't completely clear if the promotion was for food or something more exotic.

I put down the plastic murder weapon and let out a protracted sigh. "Whew, oh alright babe," I capitulated in an exhausted tone. "I guess we probably need to go."

Despite the somewhat dramatic response, I wasn't entirely appeasing Layla. Sure, I had hit my limit with the toddlers, but there was a surprising urge to go to church buried beneath the fatigue. I was opening up to God again, and honestly felt somewhat "off" on the weeks we skirted Turning Point services for some other endeavor.

In fact, I had begun volunteering with Layla from time to time, greeting the people who came to the church. And sometimes, Pastor Jake and I struck up conversations before or after the services. He almost always initiated and usually asked lots of questions. We were getting beyond the mundane niceties as if a friendship was blossoming. I let my guard down once and was about to ask him if he wanted to grab a beer sometime, but I stopped short. I wasn't quite ready for the good pastor to meet three-drink Joe just yet. Either way, Turning Point was shifting me in some unexpected ways.

I still had doubts—which I now think were healthy. A lot of people I know seem to burden their beliefs with a heavy load of zeal, pride, and judgment. There's not much consideration that viewpoints probably need to be questioned and explored. I've seen this in politics, religion, and family. I was the same, maybe still am. But I can say this… church was beginning to become viable to me again, on my own terms. I was digging in deep. I was soaking up books and documentaries. I was watching debates between Richard Dawkins and John Lennox. I was probing and investigating and, for the first time in a long time, sincerely praying.

So, after Rose's birthday party, Layla and I cleaned up the house, laid on the couch together for a brief while, and then got ready for church. Entering the doors of Turning Point that evening, my energy was almost entirely eroded. Layla and I were both depleted by the day and still mentally encumbered by the myriad of tasks waiting for us in the week ahead. But we left the building feeling somewhat lighter. It was sort of like our day wasn't complete unless we brought God into it. I shuddered at the thought. Though it might take more care and patience, I had apparently found my spiritual home.

This church was beginning to change our lives. How much, I didn't know. Now—I'll say in retrospect—I couldn't possibly fathom. Five weeks after the party, Pastor Jake popped the question.

# 10

# ...a proposition!

Shortly after Rose's birthday party, Layla and I enjoyed our first extended vacation together since becoming parents. It started taking shape earlier in the year when my friend Brian Fetzer tried to convince us that we should consider getting a group together to go to Mexico. He regaled us with stories of bribing police officers in Tijuana and running from an angry mob of prostitutes in the middle of the night.

I had seen too many episodes of *Locked Up Abroad* to take any of Fetzer's recommendations. Besides, I wouldn't put it past that guy to plant drugs on me at the airport as a practical joke. He'd hand over a pair of latex gloves to the TSA agent and say, "Make sure you're thorough; he's tried this before." Instead, we decided a tourist resort in Cozumel was the better option. Plus, Groupon was running a deal, so I was able to convince a few extra friends to join us.

In all, there were eight of us: three couples with kids at

home and two single friends with beards they brought with them. On the trip, I learned that letting parents have five days away from their children is like setting up a carnival outside of an insane asylum and then unlocking all the doors. With no diapers to change, bills to pay, or meals to cook, none of us knew what to do with ourselves. We partied like it was the end of the world. Even the two single guys—one of whom was Fetzer—were a bit frightened by our behavior at times. It was hedonism run amok.

Here are my top five things that happened in Mexico, in chronological order:

1. On the first night, our friend Tarik accepted a dare to shave all his facial hair except for his neck. For the next few days, he walked around in the hot Mexican sun with a turtleneck made of his own hair. It was the grossest thing I've ever seen.

2. On the second night, all the moms wore tight dresses and wound up dancing on a bar. A gawking twenty-four-year-old remarked how attractive they all were, to which Fetzer replied: "You know they've all had a baby come out of their vaginas, right?"

3. On the third day, I drank eleven shots of RumChata and then signed up for a push-up contest hosted by the resort. Most of the RumChata came back to say hello at push-up number 47.

4. On the fourth night, one of the couples bought marijuana from a stranger, fell asleep by the pool, and was

awakened by a guard who asked why their bodies were covered in potato chips.

5. On the fifth day, on the flight home, Fetzer kept lighting his vape pipe on the commercial airliner, which almost resulted in the crew landing the plane and arresting him.

So, after making some serious strides in my spiritual life, it took only one short vacation to remind me that I was no saint. In fact, almost everyone on the trip considered themselves "Christian," but certainly didn't act the part. Two of them were people we'd met at Turning Point.

Being a Christian is difficult. On the one hand, an untenable moral high ground has been established, which seems impossible to achieve without sacrificing much of who we are at our core. On the other hand, if we are to live out our faith in a way that's recognizable and reflective toward others, we probably shouldn't be vomiting RumChata all over the place.

We all hugged our little ones a bit tighter when we arrived home. We missed them, of course, and we also felt coated in guilt for what we had done in their absence. We returned on a Saturday, and there was a big debate the next morning about whether or not we'd go to church. I was still exorcising some demons on Saturday night, so I had no desire to be communing with rosy-cheeked church-goers—even though that doesn't exactly describe the tribe at Turning Point.

Layla was experiencing some Catholic-level guilt and felt we had no choice but to go and repent our vacation sins. We compromised on going to the evening service to give me more time to recuperate. Rose was a big help. She crapped her pants six times that day. Kids seem to have this innate sense of knowing when you need a break and ensuring they do all they can to ruin it.

I arrived at church, still groggy and hungover. I didn't want to talk to anyone. Pastor Jake was stellar as usual, helping to unlock the enigmatic secrets of scripture through spoken word. Meanwhile, I was trying not to throw up during his sermon. After the service, Layla wanted to chat with some folks she'd recently met. I took up my post in the background, hoping to be a ghost. Unfortunately, a holy man found me. Pastor Jake tapped me on the shoulder and started up a conversation that I didn't want to have. "Hey Joe, how've you been?"

"I'm good, Pastor. Never better. How 'bout you? That was a great sermon, by the way."

"Thanks. You know little Rose is about the most ridiculously cute kid I've ever seen."

"Yeah, she's pretty awesome. Even though I am absolutely ready to be done with diaper cleanup."

"I know what you mean. I changed what I hope is my last diaper ever last month. Royce was a pain in the butt to potty train, but we finally got there. After getting four kids through that, I'm done! ... Hold on just a second, Joe—"

You can't monopolize a pastor's time immediately after the service when he's trying to exchange pleasantries with fifty other people. Well, let me rephrase: you shouldn't corner a pastor and hold them hostage. It's one thing to compliment a sermon. It's quite another to spend thirty minutes complaining about the taste of the communion bread or attempting to wax philosophical to impress the spiritual leader. One of these things was about to happen to Pastor Jake; I could see it all over the woman's face. But an audiovisual tech needed to ask him a question, and somehow Pastor Jake was able to dodge the exchange.

I stole a glance from Layla, during which I gave her the nod that I was gonna head to the parking lot to start the car and get Rose settled. Just as I turned to go, there he was again. "I'm sorry, Joe. Didn't mean to cut our conversation short."

"It's okay; I totally get it. You're a man on demand."

"On demand? I like that. I've been thinking I need my own Netflix series."

"In demand. Sorry man, it's been a long day."

"No worries," he said with a smile. "I totally get it. Hey, I know you work at Pearl Brown, but what is it you do over there again?"

This conversation had a bit of a different tone than the others we'd had before. It felt like he was prepping me for something. I braced for what I thought might be some kind of ask to lead a volunteer team or maybe give the church more than $100 a month.

"I just got promoted to V.P. of Business Development a few months ago. Man, things seem to be moving at warp speed right now at the office."

"I should say so. You guys are the fastest-growing mid-sized company in the city, right?"

I was taken aback. Sure, we were experiencing rapid growth, and yes, there was a small article that had come out in the *Business Journal* describing our recent success. But only serious suits and C-Suite exec types would have bothered to read the writeup. Oh, and we weren't the fastest-growing, we were number three. Still, I was impressed that this guy read more than just the Bible to get his information.

"It has been a whirlwind, to say the least. Record year, that's for sure. But of course, with the growth comes growing pains, right? We're experiencing that right now in a big way. But I certainly can't complain—better this than stagnation."

"So true. I feel the same way. Actually, that's sort of why I wanted to talk to you tonight. I feel us on the precipice of some big things, and I need smart people to help us get to that next level organizationally. I know we've talked about this before, but I think now's the time to go for it."

"You should do it, man. There's a lot of good stuff happening at this church. I mean, the fact that my ugly mug is standing in front of you right now is evidence of that! If Layla or I can help in any way, let us know."

"Well, Joe, I've seen something in you that has me intrigued. I think you'd be a good leader. Clearly, you've been a key player at your current company. We could benefit from that experience and a fresh set of eyes."

As I had suspected, the good pastor was about to ask me for a favor. I didn't know how much longer I could hold down the remnants of nachos and alcohol swishing together in my belly. At this point, I was just hoping he'd hurry up and make the ask. So, I decided to speed things along.

"Man, you have got to quit buttering me up. What is it that you need help with? A strategic plan? Some congregant analysis? Whatever it is, I'm happy to lend my dysfunctional brain cells to the project."

"Well, yeah, we've been doing some strategic planning. I think it's time to hire an executive pastor. Basically, this is someone who can lead staff as well as handle operational functions. It's an important role that I've wanted to fill for a while now. I'm wondering if you might be interested."

"For sure. Wait. Huh?"

"You don't need to say anything for now. Just think about it. We're putting the job post up tomorrow, and you can check it out online. Let me know if you have any questions. Can we catch up for coffee next week?"

"Uh. Yeah. Ok."

"Great! I've wanted to try out that place called Grounded down on Washburn. That work for you?"

"Sure. Well…"

"Awesome. Thanks, Joe. I'll catch up with you soon!"

He left before I could object. I'm pretty sure he heard the trepidation in my voice. Or maybe he didn't. Either way, that dude was crafty. I almost couldn't move from shellshock, but then Rose started fidgeting, and I knew we had better get going before she melted down. I waited in the car for Layla, blown away as I replayed the conversation over in my mind.

# THE CHURCH WORKER

When Layla hopped into the passenger seat, she gave me a look. "What's wrong with you?" she asked.

"I think Pastor Jake just asked me to work for his church."

Then I opened the door and spewed the last of the Rum-Chata onto the church parking lot.

# 11

# discernment...

I'm reminded of a story from my days playing Little League
Baseball. When I was maybe eleven or twelve, I was playing
shortstop for the Dairy Queen Giants. No, we weren't a group of
competitive ice cream eaters. Do you remember when baseball
teams needed sponsors for uniforms? I suppose the organizers
and commissioners decided to mush together local business
names with actual Major League mascots. It made for some
interesting combinations. Now that I think back on it, one of
the best had to be the Roto-Rooter Rangers.

Anyhow, we had this player on the Dairy Queen Giants
named Angus Greer. His name was befitting. He was massive
for a twelve-year-old. But he wasn't a bully. He had a quiet,
quirky demeanor that reminded me a lot of Fezzik from *The
Princess Bride*. I was a big André the Giant fan, so naturally, I
liked Angus. Our coach, however, always seemed frustrated
by him. I suppose when you see a kid that size, you imagine

all the monstrous home runs he's going to belt out of those tiny fields on the way to the championship title.

But Angus wasn't very skilled with a baseball bat. He was even worse with a baseball glove. The only position I remember him playing was right field. Every kid in Little League knows what that means.

During one game, we were extremely shorthanded due to a surprising summer influenza that had wiped out a good portion of our team. We were playing the Bill's Tire Center Indians. Despite having one of the worst team names, they were really good. They also happened to be at full strength, unlike my team.

Most of our regular pitchers were out sick, so we got battered pretty badly during the first part of the game. The coach called on at least five or six kids to pitch just to get through the first few innings. Strangely, it ended up being one of my best games at the plate: 4 for 4 with at least a half dozen RBIs. That kept us from being run-ruled, which is where they call the game if you're down by more than ten runs after a certain number of innings.

We were in the 5th inning, losing by six runs. There were fifteen minutes left in the game. The Indians sent out their first batter in the top half of the 5th. But our pitcher's mound remained vacant. My coach realized that we had no one left to pitch. Our second baseman had taken a nasty slide into home plate and was getting iced and bandaged in the dugout. He was the last to take the mound. Every other kid who could throw had taken a turn, except our first baseman who had an injured throwing arm, and our catcher, who thought all pitchers were divas.

Then our coach scanned the outfield one more time and paused when he landed on Angus Greer. He was the last available pitcher for the Dairy Queen Giants that day. So, he signaled Angus to come to the mound. We stood and watched this lumbering man-boy trot awkwardly across the slick grass and onto the dirt of the infield. Coach handed Angus the ball, gave him a quick slap on the butt, and, I'm assuming, said a prayer under his breath.

No person I've seen before or since has looked more out of place on a baseball diamond than Angus Greer. His body was still getting used to its growth spurt, which made wearing a baseball uniform quite comical. His torso and legs lacked shape and definition. They ran together in a big blob of vertical flesh. His hands were so big that it looked like he was holding a ping pong ball in one hand and a brown leather flipper in the other. And he had a head the size of a boulder, which made wearing a "one size fits all" baseball cap tenuous, to say the least.

Angus was more pale than usual. I could visibly see his body quivering as if it was below freezing outside. But, to his credit, he shrugged his burly shoulders, stared down the batter, and dug deep as he prepared to throw the first pitch of his Little League career. He leaned back and let loose. I watched in amazement as the ball shot out… and rolled past second base.

He had released far too early, and the ball had flown backward out of his hand.

Angus shook it off, determined to get the next pitch across

the plate for a strike. He rocked back and fired again. I'm certain I saw an anthill explode. This time Angus had released too late. The ball bounced across the ground a few times like a rock skipping off the surface of a lake.

If not for his imposing size, kids would have been chattering from the opposing dugout, calling him all sorts of names. Remember, this was the 1990s. My childhood was dreadfully lacking in anti-bullying messages. As it was, there was mostly silence, broken up by pinched giggles and the sound of parents' jaws clicking as they dropped open. Angus took one more determined breath. He gazed into the catcher's mitt for what seemed like an eternity. Then he stepped one foot off the rubber and twisted dramatically, contorting his body in a way that should not have been possible for a kid his size. He curled around and released the ball again, which burst out of his hand like a rocket. It had to be going at least eighty miles per hour. I know this because it takes that kind of speed to blast a baseball helmet clean off someone's head.

The parents on the Bill's Tire Center Indians had seen enough. They started yelling for the game to be called. One father even ran onto the field and removed his kid. As an aside, I saw this sort of thing happen numerous times during my young baseball days: adults running onto the field, fights breaking out in the stands, a never-ending flurry of curse words hurled at the umpire in front of a group of eight-year-olds. Parents at my youth sporting events often seemed to be off their meds.

The umpire added a few artificial minutes to his time clock

and called the game to quell the uprising. We didn't fuss about the call; we all knew it needed to be over. We shook hands with the other team and walked back to our dugout. As we collected our gear, I looked over to the far corner of the bench and saw Angus Greer. He was bent over with his hands on his knees. And then, without warning, he wrenched forward and vomited up what looked to be an entire bag of sunflower seeds.

Here I was, feeling like Angus Greer some twenty years later. Why would someone ever call on me to "pitch" for a church?

It was a couple of days before I heard back from Pastor Jake's assistant, and this gave me time to explore what he was asking me to do. I looked up the job posting, and it did indeed include functions like overseeing church operations, strategic planning, administration, finances, and human resources. Other sections referenced the role as someone who drives mission and vision, as well as being a leader for the pastors and ministry staff.

I understood why he would want me for the operations components. Pastor Jake probably knew that I handled similar responsibilities in my current job. Other than that, I wasn't sure how I could fit.

Sure, a part of me was somewhat flattered that my spiritual leader had requested that I consider such an important role in the church. Just the consideration the pastor was giving made me think, *Hey, maybe I really am a good person.* The endorsement of a holy man certainly helps when wondering if you're doing life right.

But as I let that thought seep in, I tasted a bit of Mexico still hanging around in the back of my mouth. And I recalled the many things I'd done wrong throughout my days on this earth. It all left me pondering the ten commandments. I decided to refamiliarize myself with this infamous set of rules and take a quick moral inventory. Let's review my rating together, shall we?

1. **Don't worship any other gods.**

   Check.

2. **Don't worship any idols.**

   Questionable at best.

3. **Don't take the Lord's name in vain.**

   Guilty of this one for sure, probably every week. Random question: What about people who yell "Oh God" during sex? Seems like a gray area.

4. **Remember the Sabbath and keep it holy.**

   Uh, no. You may be the only person I know who truly "rests" on the seventh day, and it's not like you have a choice.

5. **Honor your father and mother.**

   Hmm. Obviously, that's a tough one to answer. Maybe not as much as I should have.

6. **Don't kill anyone.**

   Check.

7. **Don't commit adultery.**

   Check.

8. **Don't steal.**

   As a thirteen-year-old aspiring kleptomaniac, I had an odd affinity for taking mail that was left out on counters at the houses of my friends and family members. I wonder if I've been written out of certain people's wills for pulling that crap.

9. **Don't testify falsely against your neighbor.**

> I've never slandered anyone in my life. And with that, I just lied to you. Pretty clear where I stand on this one.

10. **Don't covet your neighbor's stuff.**

> I don't know how any American keeps this one.

So, if we judged the commandments like we do baseball, I was crushing it. Although I can't imagine that argument working out very well on Judgement Day. "Hey Jesus, did you see me? I was a career .300 hitter. Can you direct me to the Heaven Hall of Fame? It's just past the pearly gates on the left, correct?"

"Well done, my son. But you're going to need some more experience before you can play at the big-league level. I'm going to send you down to the minors for a couple thousand lifetimes. And by 'minors,' I mean… well, you know what I mean."

So, Jesus just condemned me to hell through my own baseball metaphor. That sounds about right. If nothing else, it should give you some insight into the zany level my emotions had reached during that moment in my life. At the time, working for God was such a crazy proposition that I didn't even think it was truly worth discerning. To me, this was a foregone conclusion: I wasn't going to work for a church. Well, I was 90 percent sure I wasn't going to work for a church.

# THE CHURCH WORKER

I decided to meet with Pastor Jake anyway. I could at least extend the courtesy of my answer to him face-to-face. And a part of me relished getting some one-on-one time with the pastor who had somehow gotten me to become a regular God worshiper. I had a lot of respect for the man.

As planned, we met up at the coffee shop called Grounded, which was in a gentrifying part of town. The once empty storefronts were being reclaimed by new shops and restaurants, all using a play on words for their titles. Well, all except for a lamp shop on the corner that was simply called LAMP. Looking at the shop, I realized that was the kind of thing I would do if I ever became a billionaire. Build out an entire storefront, call it LAMP, and literally sell one lamp. It's unlikely anyone would buy it, but of course, the joke would be on them because my lamp would have a genie in it—which is also the most likely scenario that I see myself becoming a billionaire.

Anyhow, I pulled up to the café and saw the pastor sitting on a metal stool by the window. I parked and headed in. I'd only ever seen Pastor Jake in church, so it was a little disarming to find him sipping a cappuccino in a coffee shop. It reminded me a bit of seeing a teacher at a supermarket when I was in elementary school. The first thought was always, "Why aren't you at school?"

I came up to Pastor Jake and shook his hand somewhat awkwardly. I looked down and took notice of the bright orange New Balance shoes he was wearing. Their color popped against the dark hardwood. His stocky build seemed less imposing outside the church, and I had a few inches on him in height.

That said, he always carried himself in a way that was both inviting and authoritative. "What's up, Joe? Can I grab you a cup of coffee?"

"Nah, you don't need to do that. I got it. I'm gonna see if they can do an iced coffee. Be right back."

I needed a little more time to ready myself to deliver my regrets to Pastor Jake. Surely, he had been told "no" many times before and was probably skilled at deflecting or, worse, flipping such responses. So, I took the extra few minutes to stock up on both caffeine and wits.

When I returned, Pastor Jake looked quizzically at the beverage in my hand.

"Yeah, I panicked and ordered an iced mocha, which apparently comes topped with half a can of whipped cream."

"Hey, no judgment here. I love whipped cream."

"Pastor Jake—"

"Come on, can you please start calling me Jake already?"

"Yeah, sorry, man. Force of habit. Respect the cloth and all. Okay, well… first, I appreciate you telling me about the job. You know Turning Point has been big for Layla and me. And I suppose I have you to thank for that. I thought I was done with church. So, thanks."

"You're welcome. But I owe you some thanks as well. I have enjoyed hanging out with you, Joe. I know it hasn't been comfortable for you to climb back up on the spiritual saddle. There's always baggage to carry."

"For sure. I probably need a luggage carousel to fit all of mine."

I don't know why, but I proceeded to unpack my bags right there in that coffee shop. I told Jake things I hadn't told him before. I told him about growing up in a massive church that had lots of rules that I couldn't seem to get right. I told him about wrestling with multiple divorces in my family, poverty at times, and even several friends and relatives being incarcerated. I told him about why I thought Christianity was dying, and how I struggled to reconcile science and religion sometimes. And then I stopped myself. "Wait, you don't really want to hear all of this, do you?"

"Actually, it's my favorite part of this job. If all I did was write sermons and try to run the church, I'd burn out quickly. I like hearing people's stories. And yours is super compelling."

"I'm not sure 'compelling' is the word I'd use to describe it, but I see what you mean. Look, man, I know I'm not the right guy for this job, but…"

"Let me stop you right there, Joe. Tell me—why did you agree to have coffee with me?"

"Honestly, I have no idea. You caught me off-guard the other day, so I just said 'yes.' Also, I've wanted to take you out for a beer for a while now, and this was about the next best thing. Now I'm starting to wish I'd brought some whiskey for this coffee."

"Ha! Make it an old-fashioned, and I'm in."

The pastor then fixed me with an unshakable gaze, like headlights to a deer. He continued. "Look, I'll tell you why I think you should consider this role. We need people like you that are a bit outside the church mold. I don't care that you have no formal ministry training. It's almost better that you don't. I've watched you and Layla dig in quickly at Turning Point. You both have a natural charisma. And I know you didn't get to where you are at Pearl Brown without being damn good at what you do."

"There you go, buttering me up again. But it's not gonna work this time. There are just too many reasons why this doesn't make sense."

"Tell me a few."

"So, hate to bring this up at the forefront, but an obvious one would be that I don't think I can take the kind of pay cut that would undoubtedly come with this job. And, from what I can surmise—I'd essentially be your right-hand man—and how well do we really know each other? Also, did I mention that I stabbed a guy once?"

"What?"

"Okay, no, I didn't really stab anyone. Ha. Just wanted to try to get the upper hand."

"Well, that's reassuring," he said, still trying to discern just how much I was joking.

"You're right, Joe. I don't know what you make, but I have no doubt the pay here is probably less. That's something you'll have to wrestle with when it comes to it. But I think I know you well enough. You're a guy with a lot of drive. A guy with a ton of imperfections, just like me. A guy who happened to get burned by the church. And a guy who I think could make a huge impact."

"You know, you're pretty good at motivational speaking. Maybe you should think about becoming a pastor."

"Ha, yeah, I thought about it a time or two. If the pay was better, I might do it."

"Touché, sir," I said.

"Listen, Joe, we have some things in the hopper. We're looking at launching another church, maybe constructing a new building, expanding our international missions—lots of cool and challenging projects. You could be at the forefront of all of that. I can help with the spiritual depth, but I can't teach the intangibles that you already have."

"That all sounds great, but I've never worked for a church. I don't have experience in the things you're talking about. For me, the phrase 'fish out of water' comes to mind. I still think you have the wrong guy."

"I don't want to talk you into anything you don't want to do. And it will be up to you to determine if you can make a few of the sacrifices that might have to happen to be part of this. But don't underestimate yourself. I know you don't see it, but you could do this. The combination of your faith story and your business experience makes you an ideal fit. Do me a favor and take some time with it, will you? Pray about it."

We talked a while longer about the inception of the church and how the pastor had almost quit dozens of times. He shared with me what it was like in the early days, and how his greatest worry was that no one would show up to the first service. And he asked my opinion on a few tactical issues, mainly about business and marketing, as it pertained to Turning Point. By the end of our forty-five-minute meeting, my brain was deep-fried. "Thanks again for coming, Joe. We'll talk soon, yeah?"

"Sure, Pastor Jake. I mean… Jake."

Then he left to go save another lost soul. Or maybe to convince someone else to do something they didn't want to do. I left thinking, *That guy is impressive… And I'm still not going to work for his church.*

In the weeks that followed, I met a few more times with Jake. Twice he brought a staff member named Diannah with him. She had been an attorney in a previous life, and I assumed her role was to impart upon me how other successful people in secular fields could end up working for a church.

Diannah carried herself with a soft confidence and an inviting demeanor. She had striking streaks of gray in her hair and dressed wildly different the two times I initially met her. The first was a lunch at an upper-end restaurant where she wore standard business attire. The second was at another coffee shop where she looked like she had just returned from painting a house. I would later learn that both of these looks pass as proper church worker attire, depending on the occasion.

During one of our encounters, Diannah slipped up. Or at least I thought she did. "Joe, this congregation will let you down sometimes." She said it in a way that intimated that I already worked for Turning Point. But she had also seemingly given me an easy way out of this ridiculous proposition. "I was more worried," Diannah said, "about how this job would color my view of the church. You know, I was thinking, 'What am I going to be exposed to when I peel back the curtain?'

As it turns out, that didn't become a huge issue for me. The staff is great. The thing to know is that the congregation has hundreds of people, all with different opinions. They'll view someone in your role as one of the gatekeepers, which means you will be fielding their suggestions as well as complaints."

Just when I thought I'd heard enough to solidify my "no" on the job answer, she pivoted. "But there's no other job I've ever had that has given me as much joy. Every single week there are stories of people whose faith leads them to do things that will blow your mind. They open up their homes to strangers. They hold someone's hand at the hospital for hours. They band together to support one person who's going through a divorce or an illness or a loss. So, as tough as it is sometimes to manage it all, I wouldn't trade it for client disputes, depositions, and appeals. I can tell you that much."

We had one of those moments that radio producers would call "dead air." Diannah's words hung over us and seemed to silence everything else around them. I was too uncomfortable to let that last very long. "Wow. Huh. I guess that's something to consider."

Jake, too, seemed to be searching for a transition. "She's right, Joe. I'm not gonna sugarcoat it for you. There will be some challenges. But as Diannah says, the staff here are committed. And, I'll keep saying it, I still think you're the ideal fit for this role."

"Again, that's a lot to consider guys. I'm going to need a minute to figure this out."

I met with Jake at least five or six times over the course of two months. The more I met with him, and with Diannah, the more questions I had. Pretty soon, I noticed that my email inbox had a growing number of correspondences from Jake and Diannah. I could tell I was being drawn in further and further. The more I tried to push away, the closer I came to think I could take the position.

Jake ended up presenting a preliminary offer so that I had something to review. As I suspected, it was a bit less than what I was making at Pearl Brown. The benefits were surprisingly good, and the time off was much more generous. But I didn't think my family could take that kind of reduction in salary. Layla, however, kept pointing out that it was still "decent money" and that the *time currency* I would gain was far more important. I was even more torn than before.

Finally, I issued an ultimatum to God. I told Layla that I had prayed about this decision for weeks. I told her that the next time we were at church, I would ask God to show me a sign that I was supposed to be part of the ministry team at Turning Point.

She replied, "Well, what the hell do you expect him to do? Have a gorgeous, glowing white dove circle around your head as you float down the church steps?"

Layla was right. What did I even mean by that? *Show me a sign...* That's the type of thing that a crazy Christian says. And yet, maybe that's exactly what I was.

Spoiler alert: there was no dove the next time we went to church. I know, hard to believe. Instead, I left church on that autumn Sunday feeling at peace with my decision. I would not be working with Jake and Diannah at Turning Point. When we got home that afternoon after lunch, I opened up our computer and began typing out what I hoped was an extremely thoughtful "no thank you" email. I felt bad that they had expended so much energy trying to convince me to take the role, so I wanted my words to honor their time.

I spent about 30 minutes typing out the communication, but it still seemed like it was missing something. So, I saved it as a draft. Rose and Layla kept me preoccupied for the remainder of the day. That night I told Layla about my decision. She was somewhat annoyed. Not by the decision itself, but because I vacillated so dramatically. By the time I told her it was a "no," I think she was ready to be done with it and move on, though I could tell a part of her was a little sad. She was cheerleading my exploration of the job the whole way in anticipation of a fresh start for me. For us.

The next morning, I woke up late and was rushed to get out of the house and off to work. I had planned to log into my personal email account from the office and email Jake my final draft before 9 a.m. Instead, I picked up the phone and called him. "Hey Joe, what's going on?"

"Hey, Jake. I just wanted to call you in person to let you know I made a decision. I'm in."

# 12

# ...the first day

Like I've told you before, I have no idea what caused me to make the phone call to Jake and tell him I was going to work for his church. It was another one of those examples of not knowing where divine intervention and impulsive decision-making intersect. Either way, I was in. And three weeks later, I started my new job.

My head was churning as I drove to the Turning Point office for my first day as a church worker. Not just a church worker, an *executive pastor*—a title I was completely uncomfortable assuming. I questioned what would happen if I failed or realized early on that I'd made a huge mistake. Would Pearl Brown take me back? Would I be able to find another job after jumping ship so quickly? Could Layla and I liquidate the house, cars, and 401ks and move to Key West to open up a snorkel stand?

I tried listening to the Bible read aloud on Bluetooth via my YouVersion app in hopes that it would get me in the proper mindset. That only served to increase my apprehension. To be fair, I shouldn't have chosen the book of Exodus as easy car listening. Amidst all the triumph of escaping slavery, it's a pretty dark book. (I've always wondered exactly how many frogs constitute a "plague of frogs.")

The plagues, in general, illustrate that God can be pretty gross sometimes when trying to get a point across. But maybe he had to do it that way. Rose captured this for me in a small measure while I was watching NFL highlights on ESPN. She was desperately seeking my attention for something, but no matter how many times she spouted, "Da-da," at increasing octaves, I didn't give her the time of day. As a final move of frustration, she picked a booger out of her nose and stuck it in my mouth. Thankfully, it wasn't a plague of boogers, but I got the gist.

Just as my car had steered itself into the parking lot of the Turning Point church several months earlier, it now seemed to autopilot against my wishes once again, and I arrived at the church office. I parked and took a deep breath. Then I picked up the tattered black Bible I had brought with me. For some reason, I thought it made me look more the part. It may have helped to have a notepad, a pen, a manila folder with some fake documents in it—really anything else. Nope, just me and my Bible, heading into the old church office to save some souls. I was a bullhorn and a bad haircut away from street preacher material.

"You have got to be freakin' kidding me!" That was the first thing I heard when I walked through the door into the main office. My cover was blown. Someone had heard about the new executive pastor, instantly sized me up, and voiced their displeasure with the hiring decision that the organization had made. Oh well. So much for first impressions. I absentmindedly made a turn back toward the parking lot when the voice caught me a second time. "That guy better not call here again!"

The woman was frail-looking, but not due to age. She had a somewhat youthful appearance, which belied the gaunt face and unusually slender arms. Her clothing seemed to hang taught in the shoulders and loose everywhere else as if she was a human coat hanger. I momentarily pondered if the Human Coat Hanger would make for a good supervillain in one of the next Marvel movies. Probably not.

"Oh, sorry. Hi, can I help you?" the woman said. She finally took notice of me and passed glances at the dirty Bible I was carrying. Maybe she surmised that I might try to sell it to her.

I read somewhere that the Bible has been printed over five billion times. Certainly, there were at least a few very successful Bible salesmen. I don't think I would have made the cut. Despite my burgeoning faith, the first time someone asked, "So, what's this book about?" my pitch would likely have been very raw.

Something like… "Listen, this book is amazing. It's about this divine being called God who creates the world and everything in it. Then he makes a man. Then he pulls some bones and stuff from the man to make a woman, and he puts them both in this utopia with pretty much all the things they'll ever need. Then the woman eats an apple, and all hell breaks loose. The man and woman create more men and women, and those men and women start doing bad stuff like murdering other men and women. Then God gives these crazy people some rules to help them out, and they follow the rules… sometimes. Then they break the rules, and God kills almost everyone. Then more people are made from the people that are left, and those people follow the rules. But then they break the rules again, and more murder and other bad things happen. There's also a talking bush, a lion tamer, and a man who gets eaten and then regurgitated by a giant fish. It's all very exciting."

"In the second part of the book, a woman gets pregnant without having sex and has a baby who turns out to be God's kid in human form. But he's also God. Anyway, this guy, Jesus, is supremely legit. He has the power of all the superheroes combined, yet with a lot more humility. He saves a bunch of people from their evil ways through his message of hope and his sweet supernatural skills. Then they kill him. In a really disturbing way. Then he comes back from the dead. Then all his protégés start spreading the word that people should quit doing all that bad shit they were doing before, because one day, he's coming back. And if you don't follow the rules, there might be mosquitoes the size of horses that come to sting you with their giant scorpion tails for five months. But if you follow what's in the book, after you die, you might get to live in this amazing place called heaven and wear white robes and be impervious to pain—depending on which translation you read. The grace of the Lord Jesus be with all."

So, I shouldn't be a Bible salesman.

Yeah, I know, that's a disturbing synopsis of the Bible. But seriously, I sometimes think we have to step back and realize that, if you dig in and read it cover to cover, it's a hard book to believe. I mean, now, after lots of life and faith exploration, I don't think I would be quite as crass in my description (unless I was trying to sell it for a profit, of course). Taken as a whole, I've come to believe it to be the inspired word of God. Frankly, a little bit of my belief comes from conversations I've had with you. It took me a long time, and still, I have doubts. But hey, I guess if it all turns out to be a very elaborate, historically connected, almost impossibly engineered farce… at least I got to be part of a great cult that tried to help people.

Anyhow, back to the first day. I introduced myself to the coat hanger lady. "Hi, I'm Joe Dasch, here to see Diannah. I'm the new… executive pastor?"

"Oh! Hi Joe. I'm Lucy. I've heard a lot about you. Let me go get Diannah."

Lucy ambled away, and I took a seat by her desk. The office was located in a separate wing of the church, almost as if Turning Point had its own West Wing. It was a bit odd that I'd never been there before. My meetings with Pastor Jake and Diannah had always taken place at a coffee shop, restaurant, or somewhere in the main part of the church.

The office lobby, if you could call it that, was small and almost mercurial in decor. The furniture seemed an odd mix of IKEA meets DIY project and with no obviously "church-like" furnishings. Missing were all the crosses and Bible verses that I had imagined would adorn the place. There was a large chalkboard painted wall that had some nifty scripted inspirational words and quotes. And there were a few annual reports, kids' ministry materials, and some books on prayer that I could see. Otherwise, it just had the look of a regular old business. Well, all except for the plush, stone-eyed, two-foot Jesus doll that sat on top of one of the bookshelves. He seemed to be mocking me.

Finally, I saw Diannah trailing behind Lucy and breathed a small sigh of relief. I felt a rapport with Diannah since she too had somehow succumbed to the charms of Pastor Jake, after having no desire to ever be a ministry person. I extended my hand, but she brushed it off and gave me a big hug instead. "It's about time, Joe! I have been telling everyone here about you."

"I hope you left out all the bad stuff," I said with a nervous smile.

She faked a laugh. "Ha. Here, let me introduce you to some of the staff. I am so excited!"

The first person I met was the youth pastor. He was wearing a T-shirt with a screen print of Pope John Paul II on it. Under the Pope's likeness, large letters scrawled the phrase: "Pope is Dope." The young pastor also sported a beard that had its own zip code. It was so consuming that when he talked, I truly could not tell where the words were coming out.

His name was Sam. "Here's the deal, Joe," his beard said, "I think we can agree that my budget needs to be increased by about a million dollars so that I can buy all the things."

As he said this, I looked down and noticed that Sam was wearing sandals. It was still November. I immediately wondered what this guy would spend a million dollars on if we gave it to him. "Sure thing, Sam. I'll grab a couple of scratch-off lottery tickets. I probably have a penny in my pocket you could use to reveal the winners."

"That sounds about right. Touché, sir."

He was quirky but had the likability that all people who get away with wearing sandals regardless of weather or occasion tend to have. We talked briefly about both having family in Texas and Tennessee, and then I was pulled away.

Diannah steered me toward a man wearing ripped jeans who had a snake tattoo on his arm. "Joe this is Flake, Bill Flake." I don't think she meant to make him sound like a character from a James Bond film, but that's kind of how it came out. I could tell she too picked up on the cadence and so she doubled back. "Sorry, everyone calls him 'Flake.'"

"Hey, Flake. I'm Joe. I'm assuming you have the best name in the office?"

"Absolutely, Joe. I mean, yeah, Bill is a pretty badass name."

"Whoa, Bill, watch your language, man."

"Oh, um, sorry?"

There was a bit of an awkward pause as he tensed up, trying to determine if the new executive pastor carrying the dirty Bible really was a prude. "I'm just messing with you man. Good to meet you, Bill-With-The-Badass Name."

The tattooed man released his breath and gave a perfunctory laugh. I learned that Bill Flake was the facilities and tech manager, and he would be one of my direct reports. We chatted for a minute or two. I was engaged in the conversation, but I also couldn't get over how out of place this guy looked. He was in his mid-forties and had a dense build on a moderately tall frame. Closer up, I could see that his snake tattoo was eating another tattoo. I kept thinking he might be a former inmate that the church took a chance on years ago. I didn't see any teardrop tattoos, so that was a good sign. I wasn't sure I'd be comfortable giving direction to someone who had committed murder.

"Don't take this the wrong way, Flake, but you don't strike me as the typical 'church facilities' guy."

"Don't take this the wrong way, Joe, but you don't strike me as the typical 'executive pastor' guy." I was going to get along just fine with Bill Flake.

After quickly greeting a few of the other staff, shaking hands, and exchanging pleasantries, Diannah took me to meet the pastors. As a congregant, I had already met these folks during my time at Turning Point. Pastor Jake couldn't replicate himself, so he needed extra hands to tend the flock. In all, there were three pastors: Jake, Erin, and Joseph. At the time, I wondered why there were three pastors when Turning Point only had two church sites. Diannah brought me in to say hello, and we clearly interrupted a meeting they were having.

"Hey guys – sorry, I just wanted to introduce you to Joe."

Simple greetings were exchanged, and I was much more reverent with the pastors than I had been with the other staff. Jake was intimidating enough, but having a checkered past also makes you feel a bit vulnerable in front of ordained people in general. Even though I was hired to oversee a lot of the aspects of their work, I felt much more the pupil than the teacher. It's like they were the McGonagall, Snape, and Slughorn to my Harry Potter. Or maybe I was Ron Weasley. It's hard to tell in these situations. Actually, I was probably Draco Malfoy.

I couldn't discern any of their ages. They all had the joyful aura of youth and generosity mixed with a hint of haggardness from seeing and hearing too many unnerving things. I placed them anywhere from twenty-seven to forty-five, with Joseph seeming to be the youngest. He was also the one who gave me the biggest scare of the day. "Man, it's great to finally meet you, Joe. Good to have another Joe around here. Oh, and I'm stoked to hear your sermon next Sunday."

"Come again?" I said in a squeaky voice to the youngish pastor.

"Yeah, Jake was telling us all about your chops on stage. Can't wait to see you in action, brother."

My face flushed, and a beaded headband of sweat immediately surrounded my forehead.

"Hmm. Uh. Yeah, okay. I'll have to talk to Jake about that."

"Great. Just let me know if you need any help with that sermon."

"Uh, yeah. Okay. I'll do that."

Do you think it's a good idea for the guy who gave that earlier biblical synopsis to get up and preach to the masses? Yeah, me neither. My entire body lit up with anxiety, and I was about ready to bolt through the brick wall onto the street like the Kool-Aid man.

Erin broke the silence. "That's your first lesson, Joe. There's probably only one Joe you can trust in this office," she said, pointing at me. They all burst into laughter.

"You should see your face!" Joseph said. "I've never seen anyone turn that red that fast."

"Oh, it's on," I said. "Just wait… when you least expect it."

"Bring it on, brother," he said with a grin.

The ice was officially broken, and we chatted for a few more minutes with a bit less sanctity hanging over the room. It was clear to me that 100 percent pious, proper preachers they were not. Maybe I had more in common with them than I thought.

Diannah finally gave me a nudge that we should go. As we walked out, I heard Joseph yell, "You know where to find me!"

I spent most of the day getting a basic orientation from Diannah. I met a few other staff in passing but didn't spend any significant time with them. Someone that stuck out to me from day one was Brooks. He was a worship leader, and I made the mistake of telling him that I played a little acoustic guitar from time to time. Diannah had to hop on a phone call, so unfortunately, I was orphaned for a good twenty minutes. Brooks took this opportunity to play me clips of every Christian song that he was contemplating adding to the regular rotation of worship.

I won't go into my general dislike of most Christian music, because that's not really what made this first encounter so unbearable. It was his demeanor. I had never before wondered what a "creepy grandma smile" would look like on a twenty-nine-year-old prematurely balding man. Now I know. Also, if you're going to plaster a smile like that for an uncomfortably extended period of time, maybe it's best not to sit so near that your knee keeps grazing the person beside you. And don't lightly place your hand on my back. Ever.

I realize now that this was just a super-exaggerated state of Brooks' true personality after having four cups of coffee. But it took me a while to get over the first encounter. He's actually a gifted musician when he doesn't make me think he might try to eat me for dinner.

Other than recalling a few colorful characters, as expected, the first day was a blur. It seems to always be that way when you begin a new job. Diannah was doing her best to explain all the systems that were in place and how the staff currently operated. She passed along passwords, important website bookmarks, contacts, keys, files, and finances. Out of all of it, the one thing I retained was a conversation about my specific role. As it turned out, it might not be as specific as planned.

She was candid about why Jake poached me. He had thought that someone from the secular business world could add great value and inject fresh insight into a growing church. But he also surmised I might need a little more growth and depth in my faith. I doubted it took a Holmesian-effort to figure that out. So, it seemed yet to be determined if I would have oversight with the pastors or even the other ministry leaders. Diannah, it appeared, was being groomed to manage the ministry areas, while I was better tasked to take care of all other operations such as finance, HR, facilities, and IT.

I think I remember saying, "Well, great, then let's drop this whole 'executive pastor' title. Less chance I'll be called upon to preach without that." Oh how little did I know.

# 13

# silent night...

I imagine getting hired to be an accountant in March is much like being hired to work for a church in November. Trial by fire, as they say. Training is scant at best, and orientation is almost non-existent. Starting a job during the busy season of any company requires a bit of flexibility and adaptability, I suppose. But the onboarding for most folks doesn't involve the birth of baby Jesus. At Turning Point, I became swiftly swallowed up in the behind-the-scenes chaos of Christmas. The introduction was stressful, inspiring, exhausting, admirable, and chocked-full of moments where God's humor was on full display. I'll never view that holiday the same way again.

Can we talk about Christmas in broad terms for a moment? It's a jolly celebration that includes obese men running around in fake white beards and red velour outfits inviting children to sit on their laps and reveal their innermost desires. It's a time when elves sit on shelves, judging kids like little devilish schoolmasters. It's a season where we go to painstaking lengths to exude cheerfulness by climbing ladders to string lights on perfectly good houses and cutting down perfectly good trees to bring them into our living rooms. It's an occasion for hanging oversized flammable socks above our fireplaces and when mistletoe magically turns into an aphrodisiac. And, of course, it's the day many people celebrate the birth of Jesus Christ, whose birthday was almost certainly on a different day.

I did a little research and discovered why Christmas is probably held in December. A long time ago, before Christians celebrated Christmas, there was a holiday called Saturnalia. This festival celebrated Saturn, the god of agriculture. To mark the occasion, people upended social order for an entire week. Slaves became masters, peasants were put in charge of the government, and all schools and businesses closed so that citizens could drink and fornicate all the livelong day. Christians naturally disapproved of some of this behavior, and eventually, the emperor Constantine got involved. After a lot of mass murder and upheaval, Saturnalia became Christmas, the day we celebrate the Lord, Jesus Christ.

Despite learning all of this, I still drive by elaborate Christmas light displays and say, "Oooh, look at those pretty lights!"

Honestly, I'm okay that we high-jacked someone else's party in favor of something a bit less hedonistic. I know a few peasants that I would not want to run my city. I also don't want to see everyone at Walmart openly having sex with one another. And how dare they cancel school for an entire month without some plan for childcare. As a parent, that may be the worst of all the Saturnalia traditions.

So, despite being a bit of a cynic and poking fun at the ludicrous ways we embrace this penultimate, jolly season in Christianity, I do think it's important to celebrate. Arguing about the exact date of Christ's birth thousands of years ago seems trivial in the grand scheme of things. And maybe it's okay to embrace the mysticism of Santa Claus if it creates a sense of joy and wonder for children. In fact, Jesus and Santa have quite a bit in common when it comes to the suspension of disbelief. I'm just banking on one being the Son of God and the other being a folk legend. (Allegedly.)

As we entered Advent, signaling the coming of Christmas, my job mostly consisted of crunching the numbers to make sure we were going to end the year on a positive financial note. I could sense that Jake was positioning me to be more of a chief operating officer than an executive pastor. We had engaged in conversations about Diannah taking on more of the ministry side while I looked after the ops, which was fine by me. But while I hunkered down to try and make sense of the scope of the organization, a flurry of activity buzzed around me.

I can't tell you how many times I was interrupted—closed door or not—to answer a question about some purchase or decision dealing with our Christmas Eve services. On a normal Sunday, Turning Point held five services: three at the South campus and two at the North campus. I learned that the North campus site had launched less than three years ago but was growing rapidly. Erin was the Campus Pastor for that site, and she was quite gifted. During the week of Christmas Eve, Turning Point held a total of nine services!

I looked up the service schedule from 2015:

> Monday, December 21, 7 p.m. – Travelers' Christmas Eve
> Tuesday, December 22, 6 p.m. – Kids' Christmas Celebration
> Thursday, December 24, 1 p.m., 3 p.m., 5 p.m., 9 p.m. – TP North Christmas Eve Thursday, December 24, 2 p.m., 8 p.m., 11 p.m. – TP South Christmas Eve

I asked Jake why in the world we had so many Christmas services. His candid answer caught me off-guard. "Joe, there are two days in the entire calendar where people who don't otherwise regularly attend church, come to church… Christmas and Easter. We can't expect them to work around our schedule; we have to work around theirs. Some people travel out of state. Others have family in town and want to spend the evening opening gifts or just catching up. We even have people who like coming to the late-night service with the entire family dressed in pajamas." (That pajama part is true by the way; I've seen it happen more than once.)

He continued. "I once met a woman who was weathering the tides of a rough divorce. She hit a breaking point on Christmas Eve when her kids had gone to stay with her ex-husband and his new girlfriend. Alone and depressed, she decided to drink her sorrows away at whatever bar happened to be open. She told me that, in the back of her mind, suicide didn't seem a faraway option. Her GPS got her sidetracked, and she wound up circling the block, looking for the dive bar that had advertised extended Christmas Eve hours online. As she sat at the stop-light, she looked over and saw people coming up the steps into a church building. In that instant, she made a choice. She turned off her navigation and pulled into a parking space next to Turning Point North. Then she slowly made her way inside."

"You'll meet this woman soon because she's on our board of directors," he said. "To make a long story short, she now is remarried and has had a baby with her second husband, whom she met at Turning Point. The entire family meets up every July in Hot Springs, Arkansas—exes and all. I introduced myself to her just after midnight on Christmas Eve two years ago, a night that quite possibly could have been her last."

"Oh, okay," was all I could muster.

Here's the thing. You might believe that the Holy Spirit guided this woman to Turning Point that night to turn her life around. And you might be right. Or it could've just been a fortuitous coincidence. But does the reason matter? The church just being there was the important thing. And I can tell you the church changed my outlook on Christmas.

I was floored by the sincerity in Pastor Jake's voice. It was his way of explaining that, yes, the church was a consumerist institution just like anything else. It has to cater to the desires of the masses in a way that compels them to show up at a time that is most convenient for them. But if it results is a positive transformation for just one person who can no longer deal with the burdens of a life gone sideways, then it's all worth it.

The woman's name, by the way, is Stacy, and I've since had

many encounters with her. She's the kind of person that rocks my skeptical mind to its core. The church saved her life; there's just no doubt about it, but that doesn't prove that the church is bona fide. Any number of interventions might have led to a similar path. All I can say is that it's stories like these that have had me wrestling with faith for so long. With every new redemption story, I start to wonder if what I've questioned my whole life might be the truth that I was seeking all along.

Back in my office, I was pondering the heaviness of my conversation with Jake. Without warning, my door flung open, and Lucy came in panting. "Joe, I just got a call from Flake! There's water everywhere in the sanctuary!"

"Oh. Uh, okay. Well, what did he say?"

"He said there's water everywhere in the sanctuary!"

"Ah, got it. I'll give him a call."

"What are we going to do? The first Christmas Eve service is five days from now!"

"Calm down, Lucy. We'll figure it out."

"Okay. But Flake says it's bad." And then she disappeared from my office.

My first thought was to check our company health insurance to make sure Xanax was covered for Lucy. Then I hopped on the phone with Bill Flake. "Flake, it's Joe. What's going on?"

"It's a shit show over here, man. There's like two inches of water. Half of the carpet is ruined."

"Sounds good. What's your plan?"

"Uh, no… it ain't 'good.' We gotta call Metro Leak and see if they can get over here."

"What can I do to help?"

"Nothing for now. Just know it's gonna cost us."

After we hung up, the floodgates really opened. Some of the water had seeped into the kids' space, so Amy, the kids' coordinator, was the next hyperventilating employee to spring into my office. Then came Brooks, who was sure the water was ruining all of his band equipment. Next was Jake, making sure I was on top of the situation. I wasn't versed in facilities management. I had absolutely no idea how to handle this problem. I had assumed Flake dealt with this kind of stuff.

But person after person kept tagging me to quarterback the situation. All I could think was: *Joe, use some common sense and don't fuck this up.* Yes, I curse at myself in my own head more than I'd like to admit.

I finally got the extent of the damage from Flake. It was going to cost $17,000 to mitigate the overflow by extending the downspout several feet and sealing a large area of the exterior brick wall that was in rough shape. Then there was the interior damage. He was right in that about half of the sanctuary carpet was soaked. It was broadloom, laid in a single sheet, covering the entire room. Frankly, it was already fairly tarnished from various stains and whatever people tracked in on their shoes.

I looked up our insurance company and called to ask our rep about the deductible. It was $5,000, but it didn't include general flood insurance—only things like sewer backup. I called Flake to see if he or Metro Leak had pinpointed where the water was entering. I asked him what it smelled like.

"It smells like someone dropped an upper decker in here," he said.

I was curious. "What's an 'upper decker'?"

"It's when someone removes the cover to the toilet tank and takes a—"

"Okay, okay. I get it. There's no way that's a real thing."

"If you say so," said Flake.

I hopped in my car and drove over to the church. Flake and I were able to trace the flooding back to a floor drain adjacent to the sanctuary. Based on the overflow, it appeared that either we had a collapsed pipe or a major clog. Either way, there was a good chance insurance would cover it.

Flake zipped over to Home Depot to rent an industrial dehumidifier while I began ripping up the carpet with Sam and Joseph, who had recently shown up. The insurance company sent an adjuster who verified the damage. I signed off on his assessment, and we immediately hired Toolman Brothers to rip up the remaining carpet and Roto-Rooter to check the pipes.

I asked if anyone knew an interior designer in the congregation who could come over on short notice and was given the contact info for Lindsey Thomas. She raced over and, as I was soaking up poop water, sketched out a design that would replace the damaged carpet with luxury vinyl tile, which would extend to a few other sections of the building. We would need to merge the flooring materials in such a way that it looked aesthetically intentional while maintaining proper acoustic qualities. Lindsey also mercifully purchased several industrial-strength candles to battle the pungent odor.

# THE CHURCH WORKER

Sam and I got to work on the outer sections of the carpet that needed to be cut while Lindsey rush-ordered the LVT. Two days later, tree roots were removed from the pipes, Toolman Brothers smoothed out the flooring and outsourced some kind of pipe sleeve to shore up a cracked section of our sewer line, and Flake hauled away all the debris from the three-day renovation project.

On December 21st, about 200 people showed up for the Travelers' Christmas Eve service. Unbeknownst to the travelers, they were walking on what used to be someone else's feces less than forty-eight hours earlier. Several people remarked at the gorgeous wood flooring that had been installed, which amazed me. I mean wood... vinyl... what's the difference, right? Despite the building woes, the worship service was very good. Jake delivered a great message, and the band led a tear-jerking version of "Silent Night" while all the people in the room held lit candles.

This would go on to be replicated at the other eight Christmas Eve services. I watched Jake, Erin, and Joseph fly around like B-52s with seemingly endless fuel. I saw the extra weight bearing down on the kids' ministry team, the connection's team, the worship bands, the volunteers, the facilities staff, and sometimes, the people who came to worship. Layla gave me a full reprieve during Christmas Eve to bounce around to each service, and I even offered to volunteer for the 11 p.m. as a greeter. I was the person I used to so loathe, smiling and handing out the programs. Not sure if all of my smiles were genuine, but I at least tried.

At 11:15 p.m., it seemed the last of the congregants had shown up, pajamas and all. I went inside and closed the outer vestibule door. I remained outside the sanctuary, catching bits and pieces of a sermon I'd now heard several times. Just a few minutes into the message, cold air burst in from outside. I turned to see a bedraggled couple stumbling into the church. Their winter coats were puffy and tattered. Both sets of eyes were glazed with a translucent film. I couldn't quite place the smell—Old Spice and burnt cigarettes, maybe? I shifted my forehead to keep my eyebrows from revealing their judgment. "Hey guys, welcome to Turning Point. Are you here for the service?"

The female of the couple gave a slurred reply. "We saw the lights on and thought we heard music. Are you, are y'all... actually, open?"

"Yep. Come on in. It just got started."

"Oh, thank God," she said.

I didn't have another interaction with this couple. They could have been overly emotional and/or soused, looking for redemption or better prospects. At the end of the service, I stepped into the back of the sanctuary as the band began playing "Silent Night." The final set of the tall white candles were lit and lifted throughout the room. Either from the flame or radiant emotion, the room felt warmer. There, in the back, stood the raggedy couple—the last ones to enter the sanctuary. They were holding their flickering candles as high as their arms would reach. Both of them were crying.

# 14

# ...church business

Christmas drained the energy out of the Turning Point staff. Sure, there were emotional deposits from vicarious exchanges, like from the curmudgeonly sixty-two-year-old man who attended church for the first time since getting spiritually burned twenty years ago. The lesbian couple who was at first trepidatious then overwhelmed by the notion of acceptance. And the single mom who realized that she didn't have to navigate life alone. These encounters were powerful but didn't displace the fatigue of performing nine special services in less than a week.

After a long holiday push, we closed the Turning Point offices from Christmas through New Year's Eve to provide the staff some time to reenergize. I worked a day or two processing incoming stock gifts and a few year-end budgeting items. The week of 'respite' was only interrupted by a late Christmas gathering; family members descended upon our happy home once again. The result was uncannily similar to the previous year's festivities.

Mom and Rachel applied every possible stratagem to gain the upper hand in their non-violent war of words. Steve and Bruce drank to be distracted. Linda and Garth left Mexican food farts all over our house without claiming them. And I could no longer accept Drew running around, shaking his little penis at everyone. My daughter was beginning to make memories and respond to stimuli. I ended up buying Drew a pair of sparkly Captain America underwear so he could play superhero instead of streaker while he was at our house.

No one wanted to talk about Rachel's diagnosis and her miraculous turnaround. The metastasis had been stymied, drugs were working, and Rachel seemed on her way to being counted among the survivors. Yet the giant cancerous elephant sat silently in the corner of the room. Maybe all of the emotions related to the matriarch's health had been run out to the point of exhaustion. Or maybe we're all a bit selfish and distracted around the holidays.

I pulled Rachel aside and quietly told her how much I appreciated her for being such a good grandmother to Rose. An awkward hug was shared. We noticed the fake plant with the red berries as we clumsily separated our embrace, eyes momentarily darting upward. I gave a wry smile at the sight of the mistletoe. Rachel responded with an unwavering look. "Uh, no," she said, in a matter of fact tone. I turned and caught my wife's dagger eyes. I highly doubt that Layla Dasch, or her mother, would have been amused by an innocent, half-inbred smooch.

# THE CHURCH WORKER

In the blink of a holiday, I found myself back at the Turning Point office. Somehow, I had made it almost two months at this job without blowing anything up or running for the hills. December had taught me to expect the unexpected. January would teach me about the business of running a church. As it turns out, we did a bit more than pray and sing "Kumbaya."

Turning Point was about a $1.2 million church operation when I started. And like most businesses, there were lots of cost controls to consider. Personnel, facility maintenance, administration, program supplies, and capital expenditures were all part of the mix. The only outlier that made the church a bit different were costs related to mission work. Well, that and the three-foot-tall multi-color confetti cannon Sam purchased for the youth program. He promised to let me shoot it at some point, but only if I agreed to wear open-toed shoes the next time I met with our bank rep.

January was also the time for setting salaries, and I had to come up with the research. I consulted the *Church Tax Law Compensation Handbook*, which cornered a dusty slot on the second shelf of the bookstand in my office. The study contained stats on most of the major roles: senior pastor, associate pastor, executive pastor, youth pastor, worship pastor, children's pastor, communications pastor, and so on. And yes, I think they were stretching the definition of "pastor" just a bit. If I had compiled the technical writing, I wouldn't have stopped short like they did. Custodial pastor, bookkeeping pastor, and nursery pastor would have been included. I noted that my new title, chief operating officer, wasn't listed. Too secular, I suppose.

Like many salary studies, everything was divided into quartiles. I used to obsess over these quadrants that determined my value, defined my worth. But no matter how far I climbed, it was never good enough. After I blew past six figures as a vice president for Pearl Brown, I was surprised at the fleeting satisfaction it brought. There was still another rung to reach for, a higher stature to be attained. In a small way, I had freed myself from the perpetual wheel of personal capitalism by taking the job at Turning Point. But the charts in the book needled my insecurities once again.

However, salary studies are limited by quantitative structures. Work-life balance, a compelling mission, flexibility, personal satisfaction—these are difficult things to measure. Even early on at Turning Point, more of the intangible boxes were being checked. I could sense a change in my availability and demeanor with Layla and Rose. Perhaps that was far more important than the hyper-focus of my career arc, and my affinity for having businesses affirm my significance through dollars. Still, based on the report, I probably should've moved to Texas when making the career shift to work for God—because everything is bigger down there, including the church salaries.

The research also highlighted a surprising discovery: pastors make more than I thought they did. Of course, compensation depends on the size of the church. Many pastors are bi-vocational, and there are several small churches with volunteer leaders in the pulpit. But once attendance gets into the thousands, pastors can make well into six figures, even clearing $250k annually. Syndicated preachers, the oft-maligned "televangelists," can make millions of dollars each year through national or global distribution of their messages and products.

Thankfully, there was governance at Turning Point, so I wasn't charged with setting the salaries. But I found myself wrestling with my research. On the one hand, yes, I think it's pretty egregious for a minister to own a twelve-bedroom mansion and a helicopter. If Jesus does return, I'm assuming he will have the power of flight, so I'm not sure why you'd need a helicopter. Also, I'm quite certain God rolls his eyes every time someone watches an old episode of *Preachers of L.A.* Surely, a line has been crossed when people start to shower their preachers with riches in a way that allows them to own a "fleet" of anything.

That said, I had to temper my own judgment, realizing that gifted orators are in short supply—particularly those whose impassioned messages resonate well and impact communities. I also understand that many spiritual teachers have completed years of study, worked hard, remained generous, and helped change lives for the better. These leaders fill a position of high stress, intense scrutiny, and navigate complicated human issues like marriage, death, suicide, divorce, addiction, and all other situations. They make a lot of sacrifices; so who am I to judge what is or is not commensurate compensation.

Fortunately, I didn't have to deal with too much resentment. After looking at the pastors' compensation for Turning Point, I thought it was pretty fair. No one was going to own a summer home in Maui on what we were paying them. As for the rest of the staff—myself included—we were all a bit below market value for our skills in the real world. But I suppose that's a sacrifice one makes to work in ministry. Still, don't think I didn't ponder the idea of enrolling in seminary. I mean, I *have* always wanted my own helipad.

Beyond the quartiles of compensation and employee titles, the operational workings were intriguing in their own right. Every week, a myriad of elements had to be pulled together to have a church service. I am sure this looks different across the spectrum of churches, so I can only speak to what I experienced in my little corner of the world at the time. And what I saw reminded me of worker bees gliding around a hive, with the pastors playing the part of the "queen bees." The only thing I don't like about that analogy is that the queen bee is the only colony member with full reproductive capacity. I'd like to think I still have that.

I noticed a rhythm to the buzzing in the office. And I was beginning to develop a greater appreciation for everything that had to happen to prepare for one worship service. For Turning Point, that meant prepping five services every week—260 events each year. The organization hummed with a regular tempo. And, at the same time, the staff swarmed in puzzling directions as the days scrambled together.

On Mondays, twenty-six staff members flew around various meetings to debrief, check-in, socialize, regroup, and plan to repeat Sunday all over again in six more days. The coffee pot worked overtime, and there were always stories being shared from the weekend. Usually, the banter soothed the concerns of people who were struggling or celebrated moments of good deeds, connection, or redemption. During my first sixty days, there were a few doozies that reminded me of God's sense of humor. To this day, I chuckle out loud any time I read the name, Marge.

An Alcoholics Anonymous group met at our North Campus on Thursday evenings at 7 p.m. I was told they had been active for two years, so there were a lot of regulars. As such, the group often left the building unlocked to accommodate late arrivals and varying schedules. On one particular evening, a somewhat unstable middle-aged woman named Marge strolled up to the front door. I imagine she was surprised to turn the handle and watch the door click open. She squeezed through the entry, carrying her bright red umbrella. It wasn't raining outside.

Marge quietly entered, not ready yet to announce her presence, and heard muffled voices coming from the basement. The AA group, mostly men in their forties and fifties, had arranged themselves into short rows facing a small wooden podium. There were about thirty of them, seated in vintage metal chairs that were the color and fade of a dark pair of blue jeans. I imagine one of the men delivering an emotionally charged testimony about the trials of addiction when he caught a flash of red out of the corner of his eye.

At the bottom of the stairs, Marge stuck the tip of her limp umbrella into the room. In a single motion, she sprang upon the AA group and pushed open the large red canopy with a *click* and a *whoosh*. She then began spinning it and prancing around the room like a possessed Mary Poppins.

"Someone stole my daughter! Have you seen my daughter?! You are all going to hell! This place is unclean! Out *demons*! Out damn you!!"

Having no defensive training against the Dark Arts, most of the group scattered. The AA leader, who I'm told had the mustache of a cowboy (whatever that means), and another older gentleman tried to reason with the woman. "Where'd you take her?" said Marge. "I'll bind you in those heavy chains, so help me God!" The men realized they were outmatched and called the police.

While the police were on their way, Marge took it upon herself to spread paper towels and black Sharpie markers all over the sanctuary. What she didn't know was that Gary, a college student we'd recently hired to spot-clean the church, was still in the building. Gary, who couldn't have been more than five-foot-five and 140 pounds, was lying on the floor of the kitchen, clutching a butcher's knife and praying. If Marge hadn't departed before the police showed up, the officers might've interrupted a medieval dual between a knife-wielding dwarf and a cackling, sun-shaded sorceress.

We found out that Marge was a known neighborhood schizophrenic who had acted strangely in other businesses but had never actually threatened anyone or been violent. Many of my colleagues were concerned about the ordeal and asked me what I thought we should do. I told them I needed a minute to think it over.

Mental illness is no joking matter, and building security needed to be taken seriously. I sat down to jot some notes, get my thoughts in order to formulate a plan. I wrote the word "Marge" on my legal pad. The laughter heaved out of me so unexpectedly that I doubled over and hit my head on the desk. Insuppressible tears streamed onto the cheap wood and soaked a finance report nestled up next to my notebook. I kept catching my breath and releasing again, the calm thwarted each time by flashes of the woman with the red umbrella, dancing around the sanctuary, showering the holy space with permanent markers and white cocktail napkins. The real-life of a church was so much stranger than fiction.

We could have filled countless hours sitting around telling stories about church shenanigans. But work needed to be done to keep the organized religion moving. After the Monday stories, the rest of the week flowed like one big bell curve of productivity.

It seemed to me that the church staff operated on a gradually increasing level of bustling from Sunday to Wednesday. But as the week dragged on, fewer staff would be present. Yes, there were a lot of outside meetings and tasks that needed tending, but it still felt like the early weekdays were the days when the flurry of preparations was most active. By Thursday, nearly half of the staff would be offsite almost the entire day. And then Fridays were the day off for everyone other than those of us who didn't have official Sunday roles (thankfully that still included me).

I found it fascinating and a bit frustrating that so much creativity, administration, and planning were crammed into so few days. But somehow the staff made it work. Worship leaders planned songs. Kids' ministry staff wrote curriculum and made trinkets. Pastors wrote sermons. Communications people made artwork and printouts. And so on.

Every employee wanted to be recognized for specific contributions, but there are only so many affirmations to go around. Jake had to prepare for sermons every week, find time to meet with congregants, make hospital visits, counsel couples, and fulfill all the normal trappings of a CEO. The same was true for the other pastors. This left Diannah and me, by and large, to hear concerns of the staff, mitigate disputes, and dole out praise and criticism as needed across the spectrum. She was better at it than I was. I often came at it with a "just shut up and do your job" mentality. This didn't play well in the church world. I quickly had to adjust my leadership style to an organization that had all the likenesses of a corporation, with the added weight of God being the centerpiece of your bylaws and the employee handbook.

I've noticed a few trends and habits early on that I now think are simply part of general church work. I bet there are about five I can come up with off the top of my head. Most have held steady since the day I started working at Turning Point. Mind if I share these observations? Of course you don't—ha. Okay, here they are:

1. We own stock in Starbucks. Or, at least, we should. I bet the average coffee intake per person each day was at least thirty ounces. And on the days when it was a dark roast, the office toilets were clocking some overtime.

2. We are freakishly devoted to meetings. Layla once got so frustrated with me that I popped my phone onto speaker mode so she could say "hello" to all the folks in the meeting I was having. She didn't believe me when I told her I had twenty-two meetings that week.

3. We overreact to anecdotal observations. "So and so told me the music is too loud." "No one likes the new paint color in the kid's area." "I know a bunch of people who have left because you said the word 'gay.'"

4. There's a lot of flexibility, but not much reprieve. I used to be Flake's backup when he went on vacation, which meant I received all alarm calls (I should say *false* alarms) from our security system. I once was called three times in the middle of the night. On the third call, I let my sleep deprivation do the talking: "God will strike them down; just turn the damn thing off."

5. I've never seen so many additions, subtractions, and shifts applied to job roles in my entire life. The Turning Point office should double as a millinery since it seems to churn out so many hats. I wish I could've introduced you to our connections coordinator/database manager/pastoral intern.

6. I know I said five, but I'm adding a sixth. I'd say it's the one I saw most, and that is: everyone is a pastor. I know, I joked about this pervasive moniker applied in the *Church Tax Law Compensation Handbook*, but it's true. Once people find out that you work for a church, it's

assumed that you have a certain level of spiritual advice and counsel to offer.

The culmination of all these quirky habits, structures, and routines played out during the first sermon series of the year. Spiritual planning, staffing systems, and multiple moving church parts collided. I enjoyed a front-row seat. The pastors had brainstormed a series called "No Pain, No Gain." It was a play on New Year's resolutions but centered around the story of Job. (I wish we could add an "e" to that guy's name. It would make the phonetics in my brain feel so much better.) At any rate, this sermon series about Job was meant to help address one of the most substantial hang-ups for Christians and non-Christians. The question: "Why is there suffering in the world?"

I'm sure you know the story of Job. I couldn't fully remember it. So, I read about his plight when they were prepping for the series. Wow, that guy Job. What a freaking trooper he was. Talk about testing a man—to have all ten of your children killed along with all of your sheep, in the same day? Seriously, why did they have to hurt the little sheep? And then you tear your clothes off and shave your head because you've been stricken with full-body shingles in addition to having just about everyone you know murdered. Job is the guy you go up to and say, "Man, I can't believe my plane is delayed by two hours." To which he replies, "My skin is on fire, and all my sons died yesterday." I guess we all need a little perspective.

Anyhow, the idea was set. We were going to talk about suffering. Yippee. It was then up to all the other departments to execute the various components of the four weekends in which we would talk about good ol' Job.

Communications people had to come up with graphics and videos that promoted the series, as well as how it would play out on social media. Kids' Ministry staff had to incorporate the concept into their lessons and make sure it was appropriate for different age groups. Worship leaders had to think of songs that would enhance the message. I suggested "Everybody Hurts" by REM.

The point is, just about everyone who worked for the church shifted what they did based on what was being preached. The production of it all made me a bit uneasy. And yet there was something symphonic about it. I learned that Turning Point was all about trying to create "defining moments," singular experiences that would trigger emotions and perhaps crack open the door to faith. That required a united effort and a lot of components harmonizing together, like a music concert. And I probably had experienced one of those "moments" myself; otherwise, I wouldn't have accepted this Job—I mean job. So, I understood the "why" behind this process—until we tried to give away miniature rubber dumbbells.

Tina, the communications director, hired a local videographer to shoot a promotional video for the series that had a brooding tone. The 90-second vignette featured a bodybuilder waking up and going to the gym, busting out all kinds of heavy weight repetitions that I could only dream of doing. Following the workout montage, the man drives home to have breakfast with his family. The cinematography shifts to a lighter tone as he sets the table with his wife. The man winces as he lowers himself into his chair. Then the camera pans down to reveal him removing the two prosthetic limbs where legs should be. He places the prosthetics on the floor, reaches out to hold the hands of his wife and two daughters, and bows his head.

I was moved by the imagery, but it caused quite the controversy in our office. For one, the bodybuilder had a tattoo of a bleeding skull on his massive left bicep. Erin thought it was somewhat inappropriate—the bleeding skull, not the bicep. Also, Tina had purchased some tiny rubber dumbbell tchotchkes from China to give out to everyone who came to worship as a reminder of the sermon. Joseph thought they were lame, which I took with a grain of salt given that he was the pastor who collected porcelain figurines from the Dollar Store.

Then Jake caught wind of the worship set and protested Brooks' decision to do an alternative rendition of the hymn "Oh, How Dark the Night That Wrapt My Spirit Round." He thought it was too dark. I wasn't sure about that, so I looked up the lyrics and saw that they included the words "woe," "trespass," and "calvary," so I was siding with Jake on that assessment.

Meanwhile, I was trying to make sure we still had money in the bank to, you know, pay people and operate as an organization. And Diannah was fielding a steady loop of complaints from other ministry staff who wanted the pastors to make up their minds already. I couldn't quite wrap my head around the debates that percolated throughout the office. Were there just too many cooks in the kitchen?

A newfound confidant attempted to impart upon me the

logic behind the madness. Turning Point's executive admin-
istrator (or was it, administrative pastor?), Angela, opened
up to me while standing next to the coffee pot one day. Part
of her role was to triage the litany of emails coming through
to the pastors. Thus, she saw all the conversations with the
congregants.

After dousing our cups with French vanilla creamer, I asked
Angela why there was so much fuss over, what seemed to me,
fairly innocuous decisions. She told me to follow her back
to her desk. Once there, she plopped down into the black
swivel chair and clicked on a data file. Angela showed me a
slew of stored email responses related to different sermons
that Jake had preached over the past year. She opened each
communication, one by one, revealing the digital emotions
of congregants poured out onto the screen:

"I don't agree with what you said today. It was borderline
blasphemous."

"Why do you talk about money? That's not your job. That's
between God and me."

"If you can't stand up and take a side on this issue, you're
not who I thought you were."

"I just wanted to let you know that Kim and Brian Littleton
are leaving the church because of what you said today."

"Please tell the band to turn the music down!"

I sat with Angela for thirty minutes, absorbing the criticism, trying to imagine how I would feel if the words were
directed at me. I must have been wearing a "run for the hills"
face because she quickly offered up some reassurance. "There

are a lot of positive emails as well, Joe. I'd file the critical ones under 'uncommon.' It's not something I see every week or even every month."

Angela showed me the more scathing reviews, I think, as a way of answering why pastors care a lot about the components that go into a service. Every week, they have the opportunity to create mountain top experiences for people. And they have an equal opportunity to offend or even ostracize.

In the end, the bicep skull was blocked out, the worship team chose a less depressing musical lineup, and somehow the pastors made the rubber dumbbell tchotchkes from China work as sermon reminders. During my time at Turning Point, I've wondered if we should cut all this out and go back to preaching under a big white tent, without the baggage of modern tools and equipment. But then, I remember that there's a difference-maker in scrutinizing and preparing every available element: warm and honest greetings, a welcoming space, compelling music, good background graphics, solid preaching, a call to action. I tasted this mixture in my moment of desperation with Layla, and it proved to be an effective elixir beyond what I could've imagined. And like I've said before, at least it's not boring.

Perhaps churches defy traditional business labels: corporation, not-for-profit, partnership. I'd describe Turning Point as a venture ecosystem. It's a community of living organisms conjoined by non-living components like capital and infrastructure. It is influenced by internal and external factors. It is fragile. It is fallible. And, at its best, there is limitless potential.

I thanked Angela for helping round out the picture for me. I gained respect for Jake, Joseph, and Erin. My COO role enabled me to be somewhat insulated, less a target. Or so I thought. It wouldn't be long before the demands of church attendees came crashing down on me as well. And I was ill-prepared for it. When Bridget Bergstrom chastises you in front of your entire staff about the color of mulch, you know you work for a church.

# 15

# some people...

My first few months at Turning Point whizzed by quickly. Or they didn't. Hard to say—brainpower only enables so many memories. Time swipes the rest. I'm sure it has stolen quite a few from you. Perhaps that's not such a bad thing. You probably wouldn't want to remember *everything*. But some life interactions have a sticky quality, attaching to the cerebellum like memory glue. For instance, I'll never forget the day someone told me I was going to "destroy everything that's green and good in this world."

It was March, and the winter had abruptly ceased, thankfully taking with it the awful windchills and unsightly street slush. Soft beds of fresh snow make an urban metropolis seem magical. But when they melt, it looks like all of the snowmen in the entire city have released their bowels onto the roads. Plus—and I know this is too much information—my nipples get painfully pointy when it's really cold outside. I already regret telling you that.

One of the things early Spring signals is that Easter is coming fast. I had been working with Bill Flake, trying to ready the grounds for the Superbowl of Christianity. Unfortunately, we had an issue with our landscaping contractor and ended up firing him. This left it up to Flake to try and manage the gardening preparations, while also repairing a soundboard, rewiring an exterior light, changing the van's oil, replacing two microphones, and getting two roof quotes since we were experiencing leaks at Turning Point North. The guy was slightly over-tasked.

I was trying to come up with a solution that fit the budget. We had already decided we needed to hire at least one part-time custodian to help with cleaning and odd jobs. But for now, it was just Flake and me left to solve any building issues whilst the rest of the ministry crew whipped in, out, and around us as if they were participants in an Easter egg hunt.

I had never pondered this before, but the first thing people size up when visiting a church is, well, the building itself. Interestingly, the initial impression is not a pensive prayer or a magnanimous message from the minister—it's a pile of rocks, bricks, or concrete shaped into a house of worship that, hopefully, folks find appealing. And if the grounds surrounding the building are unkempt, well, that says something too.

Yet, as I would experience many times, it's hard to address *all* the concerns of a church all the time. Sometimes things happen that cause certain tasks or goals to be put on the back burner for a moment. That's kind of the season we were in at Turning Point. We were probably a few positions short of being fully staffed to care for two congregations totaling about 1,000 people. The Turning Point Board of Directors had already asked me to tighten the reins as much as I could as they eyed a potential third church site. There were lots of moving parts. We were doing our best, but our best wasn't good enough for Bridget Bergstrom.

The Turning Point North site was in desperate need of an exterior makeover and also having roof issues. So, it was a matter of prioritizing. It's one thing to have a few overgrown trees, and quite another to imagine an unintended waterfall rolling down the back of the sanctuary and onto the heads of unsuspecting church-goers.

Flake and I decided to save a few dollars by simply mulching most of the exterior flower beds. He even worked with Sam to engage students to take it on as a service project so that we didn't have to pay for the labor. Since we didn't have the resources to engage a professional landscape architect, I let Flake pick the mulch and identify a new company or person to cut the grass. The rest would have to wait.

It was supposed to be a simple brown mulch, but what got delivered was black. They had already unloaded the truck while Flake was inside doing some plasterwork. There were eighty bags of the stuff, so we decided to go with it. The building's color palette wasn't exactly a fit for the black mulch, but it was fine. At least we had bought ourselves some time to plant at a later date.

The day Bridget Bergstrom showed up, I could hear her shrill voice from my office. I popped up from my desk and walked around to the entry doors where Lucy was already engaged in a heated conversation with the woman. I had never met Bridget before, but I had been warned that at some point, we would probably cross paths. Lucy caught me out of the corner of her eye as I rounded the hallway.

"Okay, never mind. Here's the person you want to speak with, Bridget," said Lucy.

"You told me he was in a meeting!"

By this time, a few other staff members had begun to gather near Lucy's desk. It was as if a married couple was arguing at a dinner party. No one interjected, but they couldn't help themselves but inch closer to get within earshot of the exchange. We humans are strangely drawn to others' conflict—especially when we can just watch it unfold without engaging. I suppose that's why reality television is so popular.

"Hey, Lucy," I said. "What's going on?"

"Joe this is—"

"Are you the person who smothered the gardens with all that ungodly black mulch!?" Bridget interjected.

"I'm Joe, and yes, unfortunately, we were delivered the wrong color. But hey, at least it wasn't orange, right? What's your name, ma'am?"

"Bridget. Bridget Bergstrom," she somehow forced out through her grimace. "So, I guess you're the one they have making the decisions about landscaping these days?"

"Well, Bridget... is it okay if I call you Bridget?" I asked without caring what her answer was. "Yes, I guess you could say that. Flake—I mean Bill Flake and I are trying to manage it while we hire a new full-service landscaping company. How can I help?"

"I know Bill Flake. He wouldn't make this kind of mistake. I told Erin that we needed to address the outside last year, but nothing happened—so a few of us took it upon ourselves to do the work. Now I come over to see if any of the perennials we planted have started to bloom, only to find a mountain of *black* wood chips everywhere. And spread very poorly I might add. Did you not think to consult the volunteers who worked so hard to beautify that property?"

I paused for a moment, primarily at the way she had annunciated the word *black*. It was either accidental or the most astonishing level of bigotry I'd ever encountered. I'd never heard someone slip in a racial epithet involving garden mulch. I decided to give her the benefit of the doubt.

"I'm really sorry, Bridget. I'm pretty new here, so I don't quite have the lay of the land and—"

"I should say not!"

"Listen, I apologize if I trampled on any of your previous work. We were kind of in a tight spot, having to fix some other issues at the church."

"You know that the mulch you installed is chock-full of cocoa, right? Are you trying to kill all the neighborhood dogs, or just destroy everything that's green and good in this world?"

The room quietly gasped. I hesitated, searching for an answer to her question. "Well, to be honest, Bridget, I am a big fan of

Kermit the Frog. And I don't think I could live with myself if I was responsible for his death."

The woman cocked her head and looked at me as though I was an alien. She scratched her curly hair for a moment, then turned to the rest of the staff as if to make an announcement. Before she spoke, her mouth slid open with the slightest of grins. "Where in the world did you all dig this guy up?"

And then she started laughing hysterically. No one else was laughing. I think they were afraid that her ire would be drawn to them next. I, too, was uneasy, and there was no way I could match the octave of her laugh. Instead, we watched as this short, rotund woman with oversized glasses stood in the middle of the room, cackling like a witch. I gave Lucy a look that said, "Look, you're the toughest person in this room, so if it goes down, I'm expecting you to save us all." I also noticed everyone starting to take slow steps backward, the kind I imagine you take when you've spotted a grizzly bear on a hiking trail.

"Whew, I haven't laughed that hard in a while. Okay, Mr. Joe, I think we can work this out. Just promise me you'll replace all that mulch?"

*Damn it. Back to square one.*

I eventually had a nice conversation with Bridget Bergstrom that day, and we parted as friends. Or so I thought. Obviously, I wasn't going to spend the money and waste all the yard work that had already been done. I basically protracted the inevitable, which eventually manifested as an even more crazed and escalating level of scrutiny from Bridget. After about a week,

I started getting emails. And then phone calls. And then she began stopping by the office or cornering me after church. Eventually, I just let Bridget Bergstrom bathe in her dislike for me. There was nothing I could do about that.

I suppose that's not entirely true. I spoke with Jake and Diannah about it, and they gave me some sage advice. They told me that this wouldn't be the last time that I'd have to manage difficult relationships or interactions. I just needed to be careful not to make promises I couldn't keep.

"The best thing you can do," said Diannah, "is to hear people out and accept their concerns. This is easier said than done. People can be crazy sometimes—especially when it comes to the church. But no matter how crazy you think they are you have to listen to them. You don't have to agree. But you have to own the conversation, admit mistakes if you've made any, and honor their opinion. Let them have their anger if they need it and move on."

I've always prided myself on being able to work well with people. I'm no genius, but there's a reason Pearl Brown kept adding to my portfolio. I was a bridge builder and a savvy arbiter of business disputes. But this was new ground. The stakes didn't seem nearly as high (I mean, we were talking about gardening for God's sake), and yet, the shared faith component meant that there was almost always at least a subtle air of seriousness when talking to people in the church.

There would be other Bridget Bergstroms or "Bergstrom-like" situations. I tried to deploy the strategy imparted upon me by Diannah, with varying results. Dana Williams, a congregant who seemed to own every shade of Lululemon pant, asked if I would clear out the sanctuary chairs and pump up the heaters so she could host a hot yoga class. One of the Alcoholics Anonymous leaders, who didn't attend the church, gave me an earful about the noisy dishwasher near their meeting room. And a random person mailed me a returned copy of our annual report with "th" circled in the third paragraph of the financial section. He wrote the letter "E" in red marker with a sticky note attached that said, "Proofread?"

In less than a year, I had gone from moderating multi-million-dollar product development deals to getting condemned for one misspelled "the" in a twelve-page church document. I was beginning to wonder about my longevity as a church worker. The challenging, and sometimes silly, human dynamics taxed my patience as the months dragged on. A few times, I peeked at job boards, thinking that a pay cut coupled with Bridget Bergstrom does not make for a lasting combination.

And even though the staff was usually easier to work with, there was indeed conflict there as well. Sometimes Turning Point North would claim that the incipient campus, Turning Point South, got all the resources. Or sometimes, the staff would lament our expense collection procedures. Even Jake got into it with me at one point over "being cheap" on a piece of audiovisual equipment he thought would enhance the sermons.

During my topsy-turviness in the summer of 2016, something happened that refocused my outlook. I had been meeting with a small group of congregants for a few months whose purpose was simply to talk about life and faith. I think most churches have groups like this, and at Turning Point, they were called "PODs." The letters stood for People Open to Discipleship. I've noticed that acronyms aren't just a cutesy way of naming church groups and government grant programs anymore. They're actually replacing our language altogether.

I keep in touch with a fun colleague from Pearl Brown, who happens to have teenage daughters. He sent me the screenshot of a text conversation his thirteen-year-old was having.

> *OMG, STFU... TMI!*
> *JK, WYWH.*
> *TTYL!*

Below the screenshot was his text message.

> *WTF man?*

He knows I hate acronyms.

Anyhow, animosity toward abbreviations aside, the POD group at Turning Point was something quite different for me. The only comparison I could loosely make was to Sunday school from when I was a kid. We know how that turned out. Yet here I was, clearing my calendar from 11:30 a.m.–1:00 p.m. every other Thursday so I could confine myself to a small room with Christians whom I'd never met.

It was uncomfortable at first. I didn't say much at all. I wasn't accustomed to being so quiet; I'm supposed to be an extrovert. But then, I also wasn't adept at chatting about Jesus with a group of strangers under the guise of fellowship either. I almost left the group after the second meeting, but Jake insisted I stick with it.

After a month or two, I began to enjoy the people in my group. I'd catch myself looking forward to it. There were about twelve of us, all various ages and backgrounds. They included Reggie, a twenty-five-year-old lesbian foster mom with a full sleeve of tattoos running down each arm. And there was Terry, a retired cop who used to be a semi-professional bowler. I swapped parent horror stories with the Sheridans, who had four kids, the last of whom they gave birth to three years ago at the age of fifty-one.

But my favorites had to be Hank and Ruth. They were an older couple who teased each other mercilessly, whether we were meeting in the privacy of someone's home or in the public spaces of restaurants and cafes. Hank was a former pilot, and he was bluntly honest about almost everything. Ruth was a former teacher, and she was bluntly honest about Hank. A few years ago, at the ripe age of seventy-three, both had started attending Turning Point. They told us that it challenged many of their assumptions about the way to practice faith and the way to view people of different races and sexual orientations. Ultimately, Turning Point challenged them to let go of the fire and brimstone that had consumed them throughout most of their church journey. Unbelievable that people can change after seven decades of setting their ways.

In June, we celebrated Hank and Ruth's fiftieth wedding anniversary together at my favorite ice cream shop, Sweet Drop. We all relished watching Ruth playfully clean up the white strands of vanilla ice cream that soaked into Hank's fuzzy beard. As an unknowing onlooker, you might've thought the two had found love late in life and were celebrating a wedding and not a wedding anniversary. I can only hope that Layla and I have that kind of affection for each other forty years from now.

Unfortunately, time isn't promised to any of us. The week after the ice cream party, Hank died.

He was in his late seventies, but it was still sudden and unexpected. And though I'd only known him a short time, I was surprised at the tears that came streaming down my cheeks after getting the news. My first thoughts went to the state of those closest to the deceased. And to that end, Ruth was almost inconsolable. She didn't seem to know how she could continue on without him.

Someone from my POD group started an email thread asking if anyone was able to help with Hank's funeral. Naturally, everyone responded, but we were a little unsure of what "help" was needed. We just assumed that the family would take care of most of the arrangements and that we would simply be there to show support and perhaps deliver a few meals to Ruth. But that's not what happened.

Hank and Ruth had been unable to have children, so there weren't any offspring to contact. We knew that the only living sibling was Hank's sister, who was stricken with Alzheimer's and confined to a nursing home. The more we peeled back the layers, the more it became clear that Ruth would have to rely almost entirely on friends to provide support during a time when she was grieving the loss of a man who she'd considered to be her best friend for more than half a century.

The realization that Hank had almost no family to mourn his passing hit me like an anvil. As many times as I had bemoaned the characters in my family, I knew they would be there for Layla and Rose if I passed away unexpectedly. And that realization led to me taking stock of those relationships. How much did I take my family for granted? And, more importantly, how did I treat them? I wonder if you've ever asked yourself those questions. I certainly could have been a better husband, brother, son, and grandson.

But this wasn't about me. It was about what happens to an old man who dies and the people who celebrate his life. And that's just what he probably was to a lot of people—another old man whose time had simply come to the end of the line. And yet it didn't play out that way. Instead, I got my first glimpse into what church people do when someone passes away.

Everyone in my small group shifted their schedules to complete various tasks for Ruth. Most took shifts so that someone was visiting with her every single day for three months, both before and after the funeral. I agreed to team up with Terry to help arrange the service and assisted Ruth in selecting the urn in which Hank's ashes would be stored. Reggie told Pastor Jake he would preside over the funeral and deliver the eulogy. That's right: she didn't ask him—she told him. I believe the threat was to come to his house and pierce his nose while he slept if he refused. I was starting to love these people.

I made sure that Flake took extra care with the sanctuary,

and he agreed to meet all the florists who were delivering arrangements to the church. Diannah, who also knew Hank and Ruth, helped spread the word to other people at Turning Point that she thought might want to pay their respects.

On the day of the funeral, 350 people showed up. It was standing room only. I vividly remember Jake's opening remarks. "Funerals can be very sad events," he said. "As a pastor, I've been a part of many of them. The most difficult ones are when I interview friends and family of the deceased, and they have a hard time describing the person who has passed. It doesn't give me much to work with. In the end, I just feel depressed, because I know that this person, who has died, probably didn't make enough space to invest in the most enriching part of life: relationships. But as I look around this packed room, and as I've talked to so many of you these last few days, such is not the case for Hank Granger. When it comes to friendship, he is one of the richest men I've ever known."

The rest of the memorial service reflected just how much Hank had impacted everyone in the room. When it was over, I thought we might have to kick people out. It seemed that no one wanted to leave. They wanted to stick around and tell stories about Hank. The more I listened, the more I realized that I would have 100 percent been that guy's best friend in a former life.

One of his buddies told me that two years ago, Hank decided on a whim that he really wanted to be Santa Claus. He rented a red cotton suit, hat, and tall black boots and headed off to the mall. He grabbed a chair and stuck it in the middle of the food court, nowhere near any of the official Christmas decorations. Hank granted wishes to about fifty kids before the mall police showed up and asked him to leave. So, he walked down to Victoria's Secret and set his chair right outside that store. He finally left when Ruth got tired of watching women, with bags full of fresh lingerie, slide around on her husband's lap.

There were lots of stories like this. It got me wondering about my own postmortem celebration. You ever give that any thought? I don't know if I would've cared that much a few years ago. But having seen Hank's funeral, I hoped I would go out in a similar way. I suppose that means I want to have it at a church, filled with all sorts of peculiar church people, comingling with the heathens, all telling hilarious stories about me. I hope I'll be remembered that way.

Of course, you certainly don't have to be a person of faith to be well-remembered or have a kickass funeral. Some would argue that the church creates division or gets in the way of this. They might be right. All I can say is that I was blown away at how a community came together on a summer day to celebrate this nutty old man and how much he meant to them. I could see it on Ruth's face. It had meant the world to her.

Maybe I could deal with a few insatiable wackos in the church. Maybe I had more left to explore with both this job and this faith. Maybe I would continue to be surprised by the people at Turning Point.

As I was thinking this, someone tapped me on the shoulder. I turned and looked down to see Bridget Bergstrom with a glare that pierced right through the lenses of her glasses. "Well, Mr. Joe Dasch, I guess I finally found you."

"Uhhh, hey Bridget. How've you been?"

"Look, I just want to say that I appreciate what y'all have done here for old Hank, God rest his soul. It was a lovely service." Shocked, I just nodded my head in response. "So, who are you planning to vote for in this election?" she continued.

"Come again?"

"I'm sure it's Hillary, right? You seem like a Hillary lover."

You know how they say that you shouldn't talk about sex, politics, and/or religion in certain situations? I'd like to think this applies specifically to funerals—at least the sex and politics part—especially when you're standing less than twenty feet from the ashes of a deceased man and his widow. But I guess nothing stops Bridget Bergstrom from speaking her mind.

After such a moving experience that had refocused my perspective, I was about to get a healthy dose of something else, because my one-year work anniversary happened to fall very close to an important date in 2016.

While sex seems to be a taboo topic for people of faith, politics and religion seem to be fornicating right out in the open.

# 16

# ...church and state

I would like to avoid talking to you about politics because that's not the reason I decided to open up to you. And I'm positive you and I aren't exactly aligned along the political spectrum. However, if Turning Point congregants taught me about the highs and lows of a local congregation, the 2016 Presidential Election revealed some of the colors of the church as an institution. And boy, do Christians enjoy their reds and blues. I only wish we'd start mixing some equal parts of yellow; then we'd have a beautiful gray. I sure do love gray.

Before I jump into that, I'd like to tell you a few things that surprised me about the capital "C" church. I became fascinated with the general trend lines after I joined Turning Point. So, I did some internet sleuth work to find out how God was faring in the 21st century thus far.

During my research, I oddly landed on a quote from a movie about the founding of the McDonald's restaurant chain in which the main character says: "McDonald's could be the new American church." I thought it would be fun to compare church to fast food to see if there was any truth to that statement. And guess what… there just might be.

I read that, in the U.S. alone, there are at least 300,000 religious congregations and about 240,000 fast-food restaurants. Most of what I could find indicated that there are around 65 million people who attend church regularly, meaning more than once a month. Guess how many people eat fast food *every day*? 80 million! Also, the biggest fast-food restaurant is Subway, with almost 25,000 stores.

So… I guess loving God isn't quite as tasty as sinking your teeth into a footlong Chicken and Bacon Ranch Melt.

There's probably a lot more we could unpack about that, but I don't want to get too off track. Mainly what I learned is that the church is so much bigger than I ever imagined it was. I suppose that's why denominations exist. Rules and regulations are needed to manage so many people, right? The downside, of course, is every group thinks their rules and regulations are the right ones, and the other groups are wrong. Or worse, heretics. There's a good old church word for ya.

But "heretic" would have been a benign slur compared to the things I read and heard in the fall of 2016. There was no way to escape the election that year—especially since I was a representative of this sweeping institution that was supposed to be building up communities and giving people hope. On many occasions, I witnessed the church at its best. Unfortunately, on many other occasions, people demonstrated just how human we all are. Or maybe just how animal our nature is.

So, I'm going to tell you what it was like inside the church world, from my perspective, during the infamous Clinton-Trump showdown, as Layla and I experienced it. I'll tell you how I saw Turning Point and "the Church" respond at large, and—of course—the many weird things that people did and said throughout all of it. One of my favorite quotes had to have been from the presidential candidate, Senator Lindsey Graham, who said: "That's the first thing I'm gonna do as president. We're gonna drink more." He might have been onto something.

The political dialogue in 2016 seemed to intensify like a hurricane. At the beginning of the year, we were hovering around a 1 or 2 on the Saffir–Simpson scale. But by the end of the year, we were a full-blown Category 5, whooshing down the constructs of collaborative conversation at over 135 knots. We had lost our damned minds.

I got caught up in the circus show just as much as everyone else during that time. Fortunately, I had the good sense not to plaster my opinions all over social media. Or maybe I was too distracted selecting my weekly costume disguises while being chased by Bridget Bergstrom. Most folks sat in the comfort of their living rooms, banging away at keyboards to vent their frustrations. Facebook became a dumpsite for some of the dumbest, most hilarious, and, every once in a while, most interesting musings I'd ever read.

Sometimes, I would take a picture or screenshot since there

was so much good material. I wanted to be able to look back and chuckle at this period in history, assuming we didn't blow ourselves up. Here's a digital conversation that Layla shared with me from her Facebook feed:

>Mitch: Can someone please explain to me how in the world one could in good conscience cast a vote for Hillary Clinton?

>Melanie: Well, maybe because she has a soul and will actually try to help people, unlike that orange-faced lunatic narcissist!

>Mitch: Melanie, you and I have talked about this before— the guy is just really tan. And I think you're mistaking narcissism for righteousness. Finally, someone who isn't afraid to drain the swamp and speak to us in plain, honest terms.

>Melanie: "Honest?!" You know there's already a website that's been created specifically to track all the lies that have come out of that idiot's mouth, right?! It's gotta be over a million by now, and we haven't even gotten to the election yet.

>Mitch: I wonder where they're housing that website. Could it be on Hillary's private server?

>Melanie: Oh sure, that again. It's like the only thing you have. You're like a minion for Trump.

>Mitch: I would totally be one of Trump's minions. I'm sure that's deplorable to you. You know I'm one of those "basket of deplorables."

Melanie: So tell me, Mr. Minion, is one of your tasks to walk
up and grab women by the pussy?

Mitch: This is getting out of hand.

Melanie: No, no, you started this. Answer the question.
Afraid your friends will think you are a misogynist?

Mitch: You need to take your pills. Don't make me go
nuclear here.

Melanie: Don't patronize me. You can't handle it, can you?
Can't believe you'd call yourself a Christian and support someone who talks like that.

Mitch: Listen to you! Your boy Barry Obama destroyed
thousands of lives with his policies.

Melanie: You are such a moron! I can't believe I'm related
to you.

Rebecca: Hey guys, wanna take this offline? It's getting a
little uncomfortable for the rest of us.

Mitch: You're so damn uppity "woke" you can't see the
forest through the trees. I can't believe I'm related
to you either!

Melanie: Screw you, Mitch!

Mitch: I'm done with you!

Rebecca: 😧

I spit part of my coffee onto the screen. Yes, watching a pair
of siblings in their thirties fight like teenagers on social media
was interesting. But seeing their friend insert a desperate, sad
emoji was priceless. It's like the little smiley face had completely
lost hope and was shedding a single tear for all humanity.

Unfortunately, this type of contentious dialogue was spreading like a virus throughout the internet. It was at once unintentionally hilarious and overtly troubling. Americans found an outlet for their fury: digital mediums that provided anonymity and multiple pages for shouting opinions. And worse, divisive encounters leaped off the screens and into our offices, homes, and social groups with increasing frequency. In a time when we truly needed to appreciate perspectives, we instead crawled into our warm echo chambers filled with what we thought were reasonable, like-minded thinkers. This even played out in my Turning Point POD group.

We were having a conversation about that famous story of Jesus going berserk on the priests in the temple, described in the book of Matthew. I'd experienced moments in the preceding months where I too wanted to walk into the office and start flipping over tables, so I was pretty stoked to dig into this dialogue. I posed an opening: "Do you think this is showing us how Jesus was prone to the extremes of human emotion just like we are?"

Before anyone could answer, Reggie decided she had something she needed to get off her chest. "I'm sorry you guys, but I just have to say that I can't believe where we are as a country right now. Is anyone else as frustrated as I am about the stuff coming out of Donald Trump's mouth? I mean, people are actually buying into it. I know we're supposed to be talking about church stuff right now, but I am terrified of what this means for me and my kids. If he gets elected, it's all over."

Nancy Sheridan almost exploded out of her seat with

agreement. "I know! It is unreal! It's giving all these racist people a voice. I can't even talk to my cousin anymore. I am so disappointed." And one by one, everyone in the room chimed in their approval. No one seemed alarmed that a spiritual conversation got highjacked in favor of shared political vitriol. Instead of trying to unpack the potential connection of humanity with a living God, we spent the next forty-five minutes talking about how Donald Trump was the devil. That's not a euphemism. Two people said it verbatim. I sat in stunned silence.

The huffing lasted so long that we didn't have time to talk about personal requests for prayer like we usually did. Our time together wound down after the last of the exasperated comments had been spewed out. Reggie came full circle with a final: "I can't even believe those people call themselves Christians." She was affirmed by the silent applause of a chorus of head nods.

Then, as we all stood to leave, Jesus Christ walked into the room and flipped over the coffee table. He threw up his arms and said, "What in the hell is wrong with you people?!"

At least that's how it went down in my head. I have this odd propensity for visually projecting these kinds of daydream scenarios in real-time. For example, sometimes, for no reason at all, I'll imagine what would happen if I tossed my entire beverage onto the face of someone who I'm having lunch with. It's really weird. But it makes me laugh inside every time. And, on occasion, I accidentally chuckle audibly—though it's usually not loud enough to raise suspicion.

Unfortunately for me, no one else saw Jesus come into

the room. They just heard: "I can't believe those people call themselves Christians." Then ten seconds of pensive, agreeable silence. Then me. "Pffff, hahaha! I know man!"

The heads immediately stopped nodding and shot concerned looks my way. I acknowledged their stares with a shrug. After a protracted, awkward pause, Nancy Sheridan's husband Tom thankfully interrupted the lull. "Okay then. Anyone want to pray for us?"

No one in the group realized that I was responding to my self-created premonition of an angry Jesus. Oh, and not that this was relevant to the conversation, but the Jesus displayed by my mind was black. And his voice sounded like Dave Chappelle. It was the best real-time daydream I've ever conjured.

As we were leaving, Terry, the retired police officer I told you about, caught me at the door. He shook my hand and curled an impish grin. At that moment, I realized he was the only other person in the group who hadn't spoken up. Terry was a Republican. And I don't think he wanted to chance the group attempting to perform an exorcism on him. I left wondering if God had given Terry temporary telepathy, so he too had seen Jesus flip over that table.

Unfortunately, my creative dream power diminished as the political season dragged into the latter part of the year. It became harder to wish away what I was seeing. Words were too strong. Empathy too inadequate. And the agitation often hit too close to home.

In September, Layla and I went to visit her extended family out on a farm to celebrate the birth of her cousin's new baby boy. The three-hour drive was two-thirds interstate and one-third sparsely traveled rural roads. I enjoyed the empty spaces, the sea of land between residential properties. The city, for all its wonderful amenities, can feel kinetically claustrophobic. Green space is limited and forced. Concrete, brick, and steel are pervasive and controlling. I smiled as we passed the sign for *Plainfield Township, Population 3,500.*

We turned off the rural highway and headed down a narrow country road flanked by wildflowers on both sides. The house came into view after a half-mile or so. Layla's cousin Jeremy lived in a beige ranch-style home with an aged picket fence running along the gravel driveway. There was a tire swing out front and a small, man-made pond off to the side.

We crunched down the driveway and parked in the grass near a faded basketball goal. I momentarily wondered how basketball was played on jagged rock. I also noticed a black pickup truck with a bumper sticker that read: SHOVE YOUR GUN CONTROL UP YOUR… next to a picture of a donkey. I decided to grab the black fleece jacket out of the back seat of our SUV. I wasn't going to walk into this party wearing my pink buttoned-up collared shirt.

I've grown up around blue-collar people my entire life and, to a large degree, that's who I am. So, it was fairly easy for me to find common ground with Layla's cousins, even if she was mortified by some of the things they were saying. Jeremy shared his colorful opinions on the upcoming election. "They just can't handle a politician that has the balls to call it out. I mean, he probably ain't gonna win, but you can be damn sure no one in my family is voting for that stank-eyed crooked bitch. I'm tired of breakin' my back to pay for these lazy ass deadbeats. That oughta be their slogan by the way: 'Why work? Vote Democrat.'"

He and his brother, Darryl, prattled on with unfiltered commentary, displaying their distaste for "lib-tards," "softies," and "damn-o-crats." Almost every sentence was preceded by a drag from a Camel Light and a sip of Coors.

Darryl truly surprised me with an ominous prediction in the midst of one of his tirades. "Look, man, I ain't never seen no politician out here. They don't care about us, man. We on our own. At least for now. It's about to be a reckoning."

I made the huge mistake of asking Jeremy and Darryl for their take on Barack Obama. You would've thought I opened the gates of hell. Eight years of pent up indignation were finally vomited up. The words came out so fast and furious it seemed their mouths had transformed into verbal machine guns. They used curse word combinations I didn't even know existed.

I got out of there relatively unscathed. I could tell they weren't fully buying my Southern accent, which I sometimes dropped into during times like this. My drawl used to be far more prominent in my youth. But when I pulled it out later in life, I'd often drop too many "y'alls," "yonders," and "might coulds" to be taken seriously. Like when I said to the cousins: "Y'all think I might could have one of those beers over yonder?" Clearly, I was out of practice. Or maybe, out of touch.

After we left, Layla apologized for her cousins' behavior. I told her it had been a while since I'd conversed with someone holding a beer can, a cigarette, and an infant at the same time. The hateful disdain was a bit much, the way they poured it on in buckets, but I don't think I'd go as far as needing an apology. I remember my extended family processing opinions in a similar way when I was younger. And honestly, I wanted to meet Layla's cousin's on common ground—not sure we found much of that ground.

I was shocked to learn from Layla on the drive home that both Darryl and Jeremy were church attenders. Well, sometimes. Layla told me that religion was more of a pastime than something her extended relatives regularly practiced. When they did attend, their spiritual commitments resided in a tiny Baptist church just up the road. We had passed it on the way to the farm. I tried to imagine forty people crammed together on a Sunday morning into that little white, barn-style church. They'd be hearing very different music and messages than I was getting at Turning Point, no doubt. I envied the freedom of their surroundings.

It would be so easy to dismiss Darryl, Jeremy, and their entire town as small-minded simpletons. And that's what many people did. Part of it is understandable. That bumper sticker on Jeremy's truck was freaking ridiculous. But you know a word I would not use to describe it: condescending. That's a word we probably all need to have tattooed on the back of our hands, in my opinion. I'm happy to go first.

Layla struggled a bit with the duality that defined her life. She had escaped small-town boredom for life in the big city. You've met her. Would you ever suspect that the woman I married used to drive ATVs and go frog giggin'? The tendency for people like Layla is to patronize their upbringing. It's not uncommon for some in her situation to describe their roots as simple and closed-minded. Some even use terms like "racist" or "misogynist."

But her background is one of the reasons Layla and I connected so quickly. If we were to plot the geography and socioeconomics of our childhoods on a piece of paper, it would probably look like that EKG machine: short spurts of momentous good fortune, followed by cataclysmic crashes into struggle and hardship. We both were stricken with this need to put distance between us and our past.

What I'm saying is that Layla and I both grew up knowing what being poor looked and felt like. We were surrounded by mostly conservative Christian people who worked hard to provide for their families. We experienced the joy and freedom of running around in yards and creeks since the internet was still young, and social media had only begun to creep into our worlds. We were given lots of rules about how to treat people, but we were never expected to be perfect. And our parents rarely talked about politics, at least not that we can remember.

We both left that life behind as we aged into adulthood. We thought we were becoming more enlightened. We got degrees and met lots of brainy people. As we entered the workforce, we were exposed to what real wealth and power looked like. Motivations shifted. New identities were created. Old interests died. Layla gave up on politics. I gave up on religion.

But the election of 2016 seemed to unearth things we had buried for so long. We found a home at Turning Point and interacted with the pain and fear of many who felt marginalized by their former communities. And at the same time, friends and family from back home masked their wounds of marginalization with machismo and straightforward intensity. And you know what? Deep down, we tried to love and understand all of them—although we failed, spectacularly, to show this.

I knew where Layla and I stood. She was a disinterested moderate, and I was a fiscally conservative, socially liberal Republicrat. But what about the Church? Again, we're talking about 300,000 congregations. How does something so large come together and craft a thoughtful, meaningful, spiritually-focused response that doesn't feel overly political? Turns out, it doesn't.

Remember how I told you about the need to get rid of those dreaded church marquee signs? Well, case in point, verbatim wording from a small church in California which used both sides of the marquee:

> *A black vote for Trump is mental illness.*
> *A white vote for Trump is pure racism.*

Forget about dinky marquee signs. When you really want to make a statement, go big. Want to know what verbiage was placed next to a giant billboard of Hillary Clinton outside a church in Texas?

> *Hillary Clinton.*
> *She will kill your babies.*

I know, those are extreme examples. But I'm telling you, I couldn't believe the way history, geography, and tradition dictated the responses of churches across the country. Pastors everywhere were coercing congregations. Videos started popping up with yammering pleas from the pulpit, asking people to cast votes, politically weaponizing the Bible. I won't say it was the norm, but it was pervasive enough to be troubling.

I think the thing that bothered me the most was the labels. Terms like "conservative," "progressive," "evangelical," and "liberal" may as well have been four-letter words, depending on who you were talking to. That is to say, when you were calling someone an "evangelical" or a "liberal," you were likely calling them an "asshole." That's the way people were using those bynames. And it was so unfortunate.

At one point during the height of the political wave, I reached out to an old friend of mine named Darrel. Unlike Layla's cousin, this Darrel happened to be a black man who had become a pastor for a church in Atlanta. We used to play football together in high school. I was the scrawny receiver, and he was the beefy linebacker. He saved my butt on more than one occasion. I asked Darrel about political stereotypes since he was surrounded by folks from both sides of the aisle.

"You know, Joe," he said, "maybe it's that we simply haven't found helpful ways to define our own conventions. Hopefully, an 'evangelical' is simply someone who believes in talking to people about God. And maybe a 'liberal' is just a person who wants people to be open to change. I'm not sure why we can't have both. I mean, I'm a fairly liberal, conservative evangelical. Ha!"

I asked Darrel if he would consider running for president. I was only half-joking.

He continued. "I sometimes wish that, as Christian pastors, we would reach out more to leaders and congregants with lenses that are different from our own. I wish I didn't get caught up so much in my own congregation's mess, and that I was bolder in challenging people to go talk to someone who doesn't look, act, or think like them. And between you and me, when I see the way the church handles politics sometimes, I wish it would just stay the hell out of it."

Darrel reminded me just how fortunate I was to have friends that are smarter than me. Life was so much harder to navigate when I thought I had all the answers.

We know what happened in 2016. Donald Trump was elected our forty-fifth president in a surprise landslide victory (at least by electoral college standards). I had scheduled a coffee meeting across town that day, Wednesday, November 9th, 2016, but the congregant canceled on me, so I made my way to the office and arrived mid-morning to see how the staff at Turning Point was handling the aftermath.

Upon entering, the first thing I noticed was the additional Kleenex tissue boxes. I quickly figured out that Lucy was the culprit, although she didn't need any herself. She is the toughest skinny person I've ever known, very tenacious for someone shaped like a coat hanger. She had figured there would be a decent number of upset staff members at Turning Point that day. God bless, did she underestimate herself.

A record number of sick days was requested, and the staff

who showed up were either zombified or gushingly dramatic. And on some level, I understood. They had witnessed who they thought was the anti-Christ assume the throne as the new American president. Some people were even saying that they thought life as we knew it would be over. I overheard two staff members unpacking the book of Revelations, trying to figure out if Trump somehow was referenced in a footnote.

Bill Flake sat quietly in the corner, typing on his computer. I decided to go over and chat with him since he seemed to be the only person who wasn't going to cry all over my sweater. "Hey bud, how you doing?"

"I'm fine," said Flake.

"What do you think about this election madness?"

"I don't wanna talk about it."

Flake stood up and walked to another part of the office that was less occupied. I followed after him. "Hey man, what's going on? I didn't mean to offend you."

"You didn't, Joe. I'm sorry. It's just, I've been listening to people this morning, and they are… well, pissed off."

"Yeah. I think a lot of folks around here didn't expect that guy to win."

"I know. But they're like, *really* upset. To the point that I wondered about calling in a counselor or something. You know?"

"I know people are upset, but has somebody crossed the line? Do I need to be worried here?"

"Never mind, man."

"Come on, Bill, I'm serious. Something's going on. I've never seen you like this."

"Okay, Joe. Can I trust you with a secret?"

"Of course."

"Well, man—I voted for Trump."

There was a long pause. I could see the hurt in his eyes. Bill Flake had been with Turning Point for several years. He felt like a Judas for casting a vote for the political candidate that he preferred. And he had spent the morning hearing people wail and moan about their distaste for the outcome.

"First off, Flake, your secret's safe with me. Secondly, that dog won't hunt on my watch. We're gonna nip this in the bud right now." Again, my Southern root desperately trying to show its muster.

We gathered the staff, or I should say half the staff and told them not to vent election frustrations in the office. It was hard. There was a lot of shock and frustration for many people. But, for others, there was quiet celebration. That's what happens in elections. There's only one winner. But it wasn't the church's place, at least I didn't think, to judge or gloat. It was time to ask questions and exert empathy on both sides. I thought it was an opportunity for the Church to bridge the divide. So that's what we talked about.

Afterward, back at my desk, Layla messaged me that Melanie and Mitch were at it again. I couldn't help myself. I hopped on my wife's social feed. The first two posts were all I needed to see.

Melanie:

Mitch:

Yeah, we still had a lot of work to do.

Jake decided to scrap his original sermon for the Sunday after the election. Instead, he preached how politics impacted the church and vice versa. He talked about how words matter: the ones used by our incoming president and the ones we used to describe those who didn't think like us politically. Were these words the kind that truly reflect our faith? It was a difficult sermon. I still can't believe he went with it.

In the end, I thought the message was exactly what was needed. I'm not a scriptural savant, and I'd probably lose verbal debates on both sides of the Christian spectrum when it comes to politics. I tend to fall back on simpler arguments, maybe ones that even Rose could understand. But what appears to be indisputable is that the greatest commandments in the entirety of that frustrating, complex, beautiful, challenging book are:

1. You shall love the Lord your God with all your heart and with all your soul and with all your mind.
2. You shall love your neighbor as yourself.

It's liberating to break things down to a preschool level. We should do it more often. In religion. In politics. In marriage. In family. And so many other situations. Love one another. Love God. And if you don't have a God, just love one another. I'm hoping it's that simple. But I'm not sure we get it.

Well, when it comes to politics (and religion), one problem may be that we just don't trust one another. I get not trusting politicians. Even though I think many truly try to perform their duty to its utmost. Still, many others are pretty despicable and stand on very thin moral ground. But pastors are different, right? As it turns out, it's quite difficult to be a modern minister of any length of service and avoid scandal. Because scandal even reached Pastor Jake.

# 17

# scandal...

Jimmy Swaggart, Tony Alamo, Dave Reynolds, Jim Bakker, Ted Haggard, Mark Driscoll... it seems like every year there are stories of church leaders, whose actions smudge the institution of religion with permanent stains. Usually, the fallout is swift and damaging. But the long-term effects latch onto tendrils that dig in for years. You obviously know about the megachurch I spent time in during my early childhood. That congregation had to be—what—5,000 strong? How many members does it have today? Zero. That's the power of a pastoral scandal.

Most of the people in my demographic have witnessed numerous falls from grace unfold during their lifetime. I'd say this came to a crescendo with *The Boston Globe's* widespread coverage of sexual abuse allegations against Catholic priests. People of faith struggled to make sense of it all. My friends who think religion is a farce were gifted a growing deck of names and events as proof of how the church is a man-made establishment built on a house of cards. I believed something similar for much of my life.

So how did that relate to the church I attended now? I had a discussion about this with a new congregant at Turning Point who had just moved from out of state. Erin pawned him off on me since she thought the two of us would find common ground on our questions and doubts. At one point during the conversation, I said, "Yeah, but the Turning Point pastors aren't like that." The moment the words left my mouth, I realized I had made a mistake. How could I know that for sure? It's likely the friends and followers of the aforementioned scandal-ridden pastors said the same thing.

But then again, how was I supposed to respond? Should I have said: "You know, I'm pretty certain the pastors here are all aboveboard. Although, it's possible Jake has a collection of human skulls in his basement, and Erin might practice witchcraft on the side. Joseph is harmless. Though someone told me they once saw a flyer with his picture as the headliner for an all-nude male review."

Those things could all be true, and I'd never know it. I suppose, on some level, I had faith in the pastors the way I was beginning to have faith in God again. This is why it was so disheartening to watch Jake get dragged into the scandal that unfolded in February of 2017. I used to revel in the publication of spiritual train wrecks, but when you get to experience it for yourself, it's not as amusing.

Well, a tiny bit of it is.

The day I found out came on the heels of a big argument I'd had with Jake. As an organization, we were extremely clunky when it came to performance reviews. They were sporadic at best. And when they did happen, it was usually a reflection of whatever work product had transpired most recently rather than taking into account the entirety of a year's work. A lot of organizations are really bad about this.

It's exacerbated in jobs where the managers or supervisors don't have much regular contact with their subordinates. It might seem to you in our discussions here that Jake and I spent a lot of time working together on Turning Point initiatives. And while that's true in many ways, I believe I was brought on to take some of the heft off his shoulders. I was thus given an extraordinary amount of autonomy and decision-making power, even early on in my tenure. Because of this, we had more of a tactical relationship.

It all came to a head when he shared a few frustrations about my leadership style. Bridget Bergstrom was an example, and that was a hot button for me. Sure, there was a lot of praise for getting us into a position to launch a new congregation or expand current ministries. But I, like a lot of employees at annual reviews, homed in on the bad stuff. My talking points took on an acerbic tone, arguing that an ongoing critique from Jake would've been helpful. Some of it was my own pride, knowing the sacrifice I'd made to do this job instead of brushing elbows with innovators of industry in a formerly blossoming career.

It's not that there was shouting or gnashing of teeth, but for the first time, it sunk in that my spiritual leader was also my boss. It was a far cry from simply showing up on Sundays to listen to his message. And I disagreed with his job assessment. I argued that he was assuming there was a fire in instances where a tiny plume of smoke had materialized. Overall, I'm sure it wasn't my finest hour. I was still learning how to be a church worker just as much as I was learning how to be a Christian. And, perhaps Jake was still honing his internal leadership style while also trying to be an external visionary.

We decided to stave off emotional responses, gather our thoughts a bit more formally, and revisit the conversation at a later date. I had Angela pencil me into Jake's calendar for a 9 a.m. chat the following week. During the days that passed, I calmed my resentment. I arrived on the morning of our meeting to a closed door. I knocked but got no answer. After about a minute, I turned the knob slowly to announce my presence. Then I stepped into his office. The top of Jake's head stared back at me. His hands were cradling it. And he was taking deep breaths, trying to hold back the tears.

Finding Jake in that state, my first thought was that someone had died. Or at the very least, a close family member had been injured or had gotten into some serious trouble. I did what most of us do. I asked Jake if everything was okay. When he didn't answer, I asked if he wanted me to come back later. When he didn't answer, I backpedaled toward the door. Then his voice stopped me. "I don't know if I'm cut out for this, Joe."

I stayed and talked to Jake for at least an hour. He told me everything. He told me about the adoration of a congregation that had instilled pride, which morphed into abuses of position. The secrecy of sins that were covered up by fear and power plays. The belittling of some of the church staff and congregants. And the two-year affair with the wife of a very good friend. He poured it all out like wine into a chalice, right up to the brim.

When he was finished, Jake asked me to pray for him. I did, somewhat reluctantly. I still didn't know if I was any good at it. And following something like that, I felt like he needed someone much more qualified. It gave me a newfound respect for priests that hear confession. Well, all the priests who have managed to keep their hands to themselves anyway.

I was a bit dazed after leaving Jake's office. It wasn't his scandal. It was Mike Tamford's; the wise and universally admired mentor that had ultimately convinced Jake to take the plunge into ministry. Jake wasn't directly involved—after all—Mike's pastoral felonies were committed 800 miles away in a different state, but seeing my boss so shaken, I had to wonder: *Was he still going to be Turning Point's pastor? Was he going to be a pastor at all?* I truly did not know. And with that thought, I had an epiphany. I should say, two epiphanies. They came in the form of questions:

1. What would Turning Point be without Pastor Jake?
2. Had I hitched my current livelihood to the coattails of one man?

My first instinct was to retreat. I jumped into my email archives to pull up my old resume. I wasn't going to go down with this sinking ship if the captain bailed out. I had my own family to look after. It was time to protect myself and what was mine.

My default to trauma or grief is typically humor. But I felt fresh out of jokes that day. Even my borderline offensive, sardonic observations couldn't find a latch point for this situation. I went to a dark place, for sure. That is until I pulled up a full-color picture of a hairy turtleneck on my computer screen.

When I had searched "resume" in my email account, the word aggregator had displayed all possible results. As you might imagine, most of them were either versions of resumes that I had saved or notes related to jobs I had applied for, including Pearl Brown and Turning Point. In the middle of the sifted emails, I saw a message from Fetzer with an interesting subject line: "I'm adding this to Tarik's resume…" I clicked on it and read the remainder of the short message. "… AND his Facebook profile. He's never going to be a senator. Ha!!"

I knew where this was going, but I opened the attachment anyway. It was a photo from our Mexico trip. Someone from our group had convinced a bartender at the resort to give us two tubes of extra-long toothpicks from the supply room. We had carefully inserted these into Tarik's thick neckbeard the day after he shaved all the other hair off his face. Fetzer had even added a couple of sun-melted Tootsie Rolls below the toothpick spikes.

I had just found out that the man I respected for giving me a new spiritual outlook on life might be questioning his vocation. I was pulling up my resume in a moment of weakness to prepare for my next life move. I was questioning the fortitude and forthrightness of pastors. I was momentarily unsure about the prospects and position of the church. And it wasn't a smart, satirical video or meme that pulled me out of the muck. It wasn't an empathetic hug or a kind, listening ear. It was the picture of my friend Tarik's massive Mexican neckbeard, filled with about 200 toothpicks. It looked like a porcupine was trying to burrow into his throat. And, thanks to Fetzer, the porcupine also appeared to be defecating onto Tarik's neck.

I saved the photo in a newly created folder on my desktop called: *For a rainy day.* Then I sent the pic to Jake. It was the oddest thing I've ever done to try and console someone.

The story broke a few weeks later. By then, the church elders had met and decided a change in leadership was needed. It wasn't national news but got fairly prominent play at the local level. The most common headline I saw was "Church Removes Pastor Amid Scandalous Allegations," or some slight variation thereof.

The articles in print and online mostly discussed the broader abuses of power, but several also hinted at the affair. The reporters clearly didn't know what I knew, or an even more salacious headline would've appeared. I mean, the man had sex with his mistress in her car while they were parked next to a school playground. How can someone do that with their best friend's wife, then turn around and give the couple advice on how to keep a marriage together? As it turns out, this Mike Tamford guy was a real piece of work.

Mike was more than a friend to Jake; he was a trusted mentor.

Mike was a religious igniter who pastored a large church of his own. He had impacted the lives of thousands of people. He had held the compass for Jake whenever it felt things might be veering off course. But now Mike had added his name to the list of fallen pastors. And he did so in spectacular fashion.

What Jake told me the day I walked into his office was that Mike had just confessed. Most of what Jake learned was supposed to be confidential, but in a moment of weakness, or maybe need, I was the recipient of all the bean spillage. Why Jake told me, particularly in light of our recent personal tension, I can't say. Maybe it was because I was simply there, in that space with him. Or maybe he thought that because I had the least amount of practiced spiritual guidance or counseling, I'd be more likely to shut up and listen. Or was it because I'd be the only one likely to send him a picture of a man with a fluffy neckbeard that had trapped a large rodent? Perhaps I'll never know.

If I thought that I would be Jake's new spiritual confidant, grappling together matters of friendship and faith—I was quickly mistaken. In the ensuing weeks, whenever I tried to bring up the scandal or simply ask how he was doing, Jake gave a curt answer and shifted the subject. In the end, I realized that I was not the kind of person who could replace Mike. Jake would have to figure that out for himself.

It was both comforting and alarming to witness how Jake had responded to news of the scandal. On the one hand, I didn't feel as bad for my initial reaction. I had also thought, "I don't think I can do this job anymore." However, the thoughts

I had about my own role and personal welfare were real. What would happen if Jake left?

I watched Mike's church closely in the days and weeks that followed. As you might expect, there was a mix of disdain, distrust, and disbelief. Of course, people left his church. I wondered if, like the church of my youth, the whole ministry would disappear thanks to one man's actions. The way congregants and staff were jumping ship—it seemed a very real probability. This did not come to pass.

New leaders rose up, in surprisingly short order. Resiliency gained momentum as time passed. Mike's churched wobbled but didn't break. Considerable healing was needed, I'm sure. But it looked as though the organization realized that greater were the sum of its parts. Or, in this case, that a mission was more important than the errancy of one man. They still had families to steward, charitable endeavors to fulfill, work to be done. Could the crash still come? Sure. But I derived a bit of optimism watching this unfold from afar.

Jake eventually normalized, although a bit of his spark was snuffed out. I could tell the ordeal had shaken him, because—in his gut—he felt *one bad decision, and that'll be me.* That's a hard line to tow. "Maybe there's a reason," he once said, "that the average lifespan of a pastor is less than five years."

Was the same true for me? It had barely been a year, and already I had questioned my vocational shift multiple times. I suppose it takes a great deal of determination to be in ministry for an extended period. And for that matter, a practicing Christian.

# THE CHURCH WORKER

Believing in God is difficult. At least I think it is. I didn't soak in the tradition of my childhood, accepting without question its authority. Instead, I rejected it. And when I did return to it, I tormented myself with all sorts of queries about its authenticity. It has felt like a long road without a true destination to satisfy my curiosity.

But then, simply being socialized into a belief system was never going to be my route. I refused to accept the auto-production, the pre-destination assigned by my geography and upbringing. Sometimes to a fault. Instead, I eventually decided to undertake the simple task of decoding a 3,000-year-old oral history to determine if there was enough interconnected, evidentiary support to christen it the Holy Word of God—and not a mystical religion built on fantasy. So yeah, it appears as though I've taken the red pill, which is a more complicated path.

Let me pause that thought. I'm going to need to sneak a bottle of Woodford Reserve in here if we continue down this conversational rabbit hole. You don't perchance have any booze in here, do you? … That's too bad. We both could've benefitted from a little light libation before jumping into this chat. I guess I'll settle for this stale cup of coffee that tastes like a batch of instant Folgers from 1987. It, too, is something I'd describe as scandalous.

Anyhow, I ended up in a conversation with Sam, the youth pastor, soon after the scandal broke. He was helpful in pulling me out of the funk of gossip and calamity. He had read about the demise of Mike Tamford's church. I took him out to lunch one day to vent and to collect his thoughts. We ended up at

TGI Friday's for the $8 lunch special. That's what happens when you let a youth pastor choose your restaurant destination.

"Joe," he said, "I've been thinking a lot about this. And for some reason, I keep coming back to O.J. Simpson."

"Okay. That's random."

"For sure. I mean, if that's too uncomfortable, we can just go with Richard Nixon or Bernie Madoff or Jerry Sandusky or every single one of those Enron a-holes."

"Who's Sandusky again? Is he the Penn State guy?"

"I'd say he's the sex abuse guy, but let's not split hairs. Point being, I've been wondering how all those shameful peeps are different from Jake's friend, the good pastor from Colorado who couldn't keep his hands off his best friend's wife."

"Fair enough. What'd you come up with?"

"That none of it matters."

"And here I thought I was the pessimist at the table."

"What I mean is, for all the scandals in the world, if you take faith out of the equation, why does it matter? It basically just boils down then to how I feel about one situation or the other. Whether or not something is 'scandalous.' I mean, it's kind of arbitrary, right?"

"Hmm, that's either really wise or extremely 'churchy.' The beard makes you seem wiser, especially as you continue growing it out. Looks like you could hide a small dog in that thing."

"Well, my girlfriend had to keep pulling pieces of lettuce and cheese out of it when we were eating nachos last night. I'm not sure how much longer I can get away with it."

"Layla hates the way I look with a beard. But she had to

pluck a really long hair out of my ear last night, so that's probably worse. I'm glad we can talk about this before we dive into lunch, by the way."

I liked hanging out with Sam. The conversations were always a fun mix of honest and absurd. He's got a way of keeping things light-hearted. I guess that comes in handy when you're trying to help teenagers navigate high school. He's also smart. And this time, I wanted to probe a bit further into his serious side. "I like your take on the whole moral guidance deal," I said. "I'm sure I've let my own personal feelings and opinions cast judgment lots of times. But then what do you do about this Mike situation? Isn't that what all non-Christians keep saying—that the church is full of hypocrites?"

"Uh, yeah. I'm assuming two of them are sitting right here. The students I work with talk about this all the time. It's not always popular to jump right out there and start telling people that you're a Christ-follower. There are a lot of loaded labels that come with that these days. I mean, many of the kids I talk to can't even start dating someone unless they Snapchat a naked picture of themselves. I do my best to talk them through it. I'm surprised they even take advice from a twenty-nine-year-old with the facial hair of a well-aged grandpa."

Sam continued.

"As for this fall-from-grace deal, Mike did a really bad thing. He should've been removed from his church, probably years ago. But aren't we supposed to forgive and pray for him in the hopes that he can be better? If I ever do something as dumb as he did, I hope that kind of grace will be given to me.

I doubt I'm gonna get it from the world. Or even from the Church. But I know I'll get it from God."

I paused a minute, taking in his monologue.

"They teach you all that in seminary?" I asked.

"Ha, yeah right! We've got a long way to go in how we formally train people like me. We spend way too much time dissecting the theory of secularism and not enough time on what's actually happening. Don't get me started on that."

"Well, you can answer that a lot better than I could. But I think I get it. You're basically saying if Mike was Bernie Madoff, and I didn't care about Christianity, I'd probably just want to see him publicly flogged with a belt made from his own stolen money. The coins, not the bills."

"Sure, something like that."

Then Sam took a huge bite of his hamburger. A piece of the sliced tomato popped out and broke away. The pink seeds and slimy juice dripped, slowly, into his spongy beard. I could tell he didn't notice. I set my sandwich back down on my plate and took a moment to not to throw up. I rescinded my earlier proclamation. Sam needed to shave that nasty ass beard.

Hygiene aside, Sam was making some sense. I would certainly count myself among the truly imperfect people of the world. And I think the Church is full of people like me. We're personifications of the hypocritical Christians that others often talk about. Perpetually, I was inhabited by cursing, lying, impure thoughts, and poor behaviors. However, these church people—the ones I interacted with every day—accepted me anyway. I wasn't just trying to be a better person. I was trying to understand why I deserved any grace at all.

It's not that I don't have "good" in me. I think I'm generally a decent person. But up until rekindling my faith at Turning Point, I didn't know what was guiding me other than my opinions of what was moral or immoral. I made up my own rules, made up my own mind about how I should treat other people. I fixated on my personal process for responding to tough life issues like love, loss, loneliness, addiction, sexuality, violence, etc. I was my own god. And it felt very freeing. For a while—until I bumped up against these things. That's when I learned that I make a really, really shitty god.

As we were paying our checks in the depressingly dated TGI Friday's restaurant, I decided to confide in Sam. I had one more thing I needed to get off my chest. "Hey man, I need to level with you. I don't know how I ended up working here. Don't get me wrong, I've had some really high moments and learned a ton, but I tend to believe I'm much closer on the spectrum to someone like Mike than, say, you or Jake. Pretend I'm one of the teenagers that comes to you for advice. What would you say to me about that?"

Sam took a deep breath. "Well, Joe, first let me just say that you're about the ugliest teenager I've ever met. And how many times have you repeated your senior year? You look old. It's time to move on man. Your glassy-eyed, middle-aged stare is starting to scare some of the cheerleaders."

The surge of laughter opened the flap of my windpipe. I gurgled up several ounces of water, the rest spilling out of my nose in a half-sneeze. The choking fit lasted so long that, at one point, our server came over and offered me a cough drop. I'm sure she was hoping that it would help expedite our departure.

"I'll be honest, Joe, I never get that kind of reaction from my students. Bravo." He waited for me to catch my breath, then doubled back. "Okay, here's the deal. The fact that you're even willing to admit that tells me you're a better Christian than a lot of people I know. It means you can relate to the Mikes of the world and understand their pain when they screw up. Most of us suck at that. And if you think seminary training and ministry experience make Jake and me better people than you, just come visit my brain some time. Well, maybe don't do that. You might come out lobotomized."

"I don't want to ever see the inside of your head," I said, still coughing.

"Seriously though, man, I'm glad you work at Turning Point. I know how awkward it is to work for a church. People shoot peculiar looks when you tell them what you do for a living. They quit cursing, and their buttholes immediately pucker up to make their bodies appear statelier. But don't worry too much about figuring it all out. Just keep talking about your faith in the way you do now. Help make being a Christian just a little less weird. Or at least, I mean, 'weird' in a good way."

We got a final glare from our server. Then we shimmied out of our booth and headed back to the office.

I still didn't know how long I'd feel comfortable or appropriate working for a church. But I had to admit, I was fortunate to be surrounded by people who welcomed these kinds of real conversations. Sure, I missed some of the glamour of hobnobbing with super-smart tech start-up wizards and working on visionary projects with ingenious creatives. Yet, I can't recall having a single interaction with any of them about the meaning of life. Now, that was ingrained in my work—the acceptance to probe and postulate and ponder.

People like Flake, Sam, Jake, Diannah, and many of my other colleagues were beginning to have a profound effect on me. They upended so many of my notions and assumptions about religion and religious people. I was finally ready to at least talk to people about God again. And not just as a matter of reciprocity. Maybe I could start the conversation myself. Maybe I was as ready as I'd ever be to lead a dialogue. Maybe it wouldn't be as disastrous as I imagined.

It's all fine and dandy to think that way until you actually have to put your money where your mouth is. I thought about the ludicrous omen on my first day at Turning Point—when Joseph had ribbed me about preaching a sermon. I never had to stand and deliver from the pulpit. But I soon figured out that I wasn't quite ready to talk about God in an authoritative way in public. At least not in front of 175 people at a bar. Especially when a drunken old man throws a bucket of peanuts at someone's head on a hot summer evening.

# 18

# Barvangelism

The summer of 2017 came on fast and was blazing hot. That's the thing about living in a place with four distinct seasons. The weather shifts quickly, like a race car throttling into a new gear. Lamentations abound as everyone feels cheated by the short ride through the beautiful spring and fall weather. The less desirable seasons seem longer and more brutal each time around. The summer, which thickens the air with humidity, feels hotter than the year before. The winter, which suffocates the mild autumn, arrives "colder than a polar bear's toenails." That's my favorite way to describe winter, by the way. I celebrate the entire catalog of the band Outkast. I doubt you know a lot of their stuff. Before I leave here, I'm definitely going to play "Ms. Jackson" for you. I am for real.

I'm not sure I enjoy the weather where I live, but I acknowledge the barometer of perspective. My neighbors have to endure the extremes to fully appreciate the blissful shoulder seasons, the tight windows where conditions are just right. A frosty craft beer glistening on a shaded outdoor patio can be euphoric. But a second-degree burn from a scalding hot steering wheel is hellish. Likewise, watching chunky snowflakes rain down in a pristine white blanket across the neighborhood is delightful. Snot frozen to a crusted goo on the upper lip is repulsive.

Attendance at Turning Point changed during the seasons, just like the weather, or perhaps like semesters at school. I was racing toward the completion of my second year; almost two full cycles of ministry were under my belt, and I had become intrigued by when people did and did not show up for church. The emerging pattern appeared to be pervasive. In talking with other ministry people, they too experienced similar ebbs and flows. Here's my crude attempt at creating an outline for a publication that someone should assemble on the subject. Let's call it: *The Christian Attender's Almanac: Anecdotes on Church Participation.* The subtitle: *A Pastor's Guide to Frustration.*

> **January –** One of my New Year's resolutions is to be a better person. I'm going to go to church every week.
> **February –** Okay, I didn't mean every week. I'll go to church every other week. I should also cancel my gym membership, but that would mean I have to pick up the phone and call someone.
> **March –** I would go to church today if only I could find my umbrella. I can't wait for spring break. Wait, do

I still get spring break? My kids get spring break. Damn those kids are spoiled.

**April –** I should invite my sister to come with me to Easter. She needs some Jesus in her life for sure. And I definitely need to start planning my summer vacation before it's too late.

**May –** I really need to cut the grass. While I'm at it, I should build a retaining wall, add a bird feeder, and plant a vegetable garden. I think I can get all that done this Sunday if I skip church just this once.

**June –** Yay! Disneyland for ten days! When I get back, I'm going to show the pastor all the pictures from our trip!

**July –** Yay! Beach chair and margaritas, here I come! Oh wait, Brandon has that summer baseball league with triple headers for eight Sundays in a row. Man, it feels like I haven't been to church at all lately.

**August –** I wonder if I can squeeze in one more vacation? It'll have to be somewhere within driving distance. Maybe a quick three-day weekend. Hey, maybe I'll check out another church while I'm out of town.

**September –** I feel bad that I didn't check out any churches while I was out of town. I should get back on the horse and refresh my New Year's resolutions. I'll start by going to church every Sunday this month. Well, at least two Sundays.

**October –** Hey, Halloween is coming up! Is that still "the

Day of the Devil?" I'll at least go to the Trunk-or-Treat my church is hosting in that dirty parking lot.

**November –** I'm going to meet with the pastor every week this month to prepare for Thanksgiving. I hope Uncle Brad doesn't beam me with his weird, far-off stare again this year while the turkey is being carved.

**December –** I feel so guilty about spending all this money on Christmas gifts. I need to go to church to repent. Oh, and I should invite everyone I know to come to the Christmas Eve service. And then never invite them to anything else that happens at church for the rest of the year—except maybe Easter.

It's a work in progress, but you get the idea.

As it was, we were enveloped in a torrid, seemingly endless summer. The school year was starting back up for most of the region, and the Turning Point seats were filling more often. Fall was especially active for the kids' ministry folks. We had one full-time and one part-time employee to manage the children at both sites. On an average Sunday, there could easily be 200 kids across all the services. I thought it was a bit like running a daycare that only opens one day each week and staffed with teachers who don't make any money. Volunteers were undeniably keeping the ship afloat.

Amy and Grace—the two kids' ministry coordinators—put a lot of effort into every class, making each exercise meaningful and age-appropriate. They constantly recruited volunteers and tried to create consistency for the children. They commanded small armies of craft project preparers, with ammunition in the form of scissors, cardstock, glue, dry macaroni, and cotton balls spread out all across their war room. It was quite the operation.

The volunteers at Turning Point, like those in kids' ministry, were undeniably essential. They were the people I saw greeting the guests, making the coffee, helping with parking, wrangling the young ones, and tidying the spaces. In a pinch, they also cleaned vomit off the floor—which I witnessed twice. But like paid positions, there is turnover with volunteers. Folks get burned out or have a life-altering event. They move, get sick, or sometimes find another church. This is why Turning Point, under Jake, was so focused on inviting new people. "Churches die because they get complacent," he said to me once. "They get rooted in comfort, averse to change, and lose their zest to invite new people to be part of something bigger than themselves."

Jake is an entrepreneurial evangelist. He's always looking for ideas that can reach new people, draw them out of their comfort zones. I got to take part in one of these brainstorms recently. Walking back to my desk from the bathroom, Jake grabbed me on the shoulder and asked if I could join him in Turning Point's conference room. He had circled up Joseph and Brooks as well. I followed him around the corner and reflexively stepped over a dark stain on the carpet as I entered the room. I took a seat next to Joseph at the thick red table with the "hand-me-down" appearance.

The walls were close. The room was rectangular, thin, and stifling. I'd held meetings with the finance committee in this tired space many times. It desperately needed an upgrade. I suppose the tattered look of certain facilities gives the impression that our work was not yet done, and we still needed those tithes and offerings to keep flowing. Our conference room had quite a different presentation than the luminous, modern contemporary offices at Pearl Brown.

Jake started the meeting with a brief introduction then launched into the collective sharing of ideas. Banter began slowly, no one wanting to open their mouth and say something stupid. But soon enough, we resembled a crazed game of Pictionary, type-A personalities spewing out suggestions from every direction. All concepts were considered. Tangents were encouraged. Brooks showcased ever-expanding pit stains under his yellow shirt each time he raised his arms in excitement.

After thirty minutes, the chatter began to fade. A lull came on abruptly, and we sat quietly for a moment, trying to decipher the scribblings. The penmanship and clusters of colors created an interesting tapestry. If we had given a group of kindergarteners their own set of EXPO Low-Odor Dry Erase Markers, they would have done better.

Joseph stood up unexpectedly and began circling words, seemingly at random. He stopped short after only three: *beer, Bible, podcast.* I believe "beer" had been a late addition, tossed into the delirium of a winding down idea session. "A live theology podcast at a brewery!" Joseph blurted excitedly. He let his goofy smile and raised eyebrows stick for a moment. I think he was expecting the room to slow clap into whoops of affirmation.

Several seconds passed, then Brooks chimed in. "A live, *interactive* theology podcast."

"Well, hell, may as well throw in a debate while you're at it," I said. My hint of sarcasm was so subtle that no one caught on. I half-thought Joseph and Brooks were joking. I expected a quippy remark, and then we'd move onto to better ideas.

Then Jake added his reaction. "Yes! Love it!"

So, I was wrong. It didn't take long for them to land on the venue either. Grins expanded at the mention of Cotch Hops, the popular new brewery with no-nonsense lagers, ales, stouts, and dunkels. Earlier in the year, I had gone to the Cotch Hops' grand opening. I could almost taste the strong aroma of hops and barley settling over the raw steel beams, aged wood furniture, and burnished kilns. It was a very cool space, but not something one would associate with Christians.

There's nothing inherently novel about churches hosting events in non-traditional settings. Religious groups show up at festivals, schools, restaurants, bars, and parks. Time and place are important to keep things from getting out of hand. Like, if you find yourself standing on top of a shipping crate at Octoberfest shouting scriptures into a bull horn… maybe it's time to reconsider a few life choices. I'll give those people credit. It takes some cojones to practice that kind of extreme evangelism. However, tipsy dispositions and swishy, full bladders tend to limit concentration. Most of my cognitive functions shut down when my brain is screaming *must pee, must pee, must pee.*

So, a live podcast theology debate poured over a cold pint? I'll admit it. I was intrigued. Either way, Jake's reaction told me we were about to run with the concept. But what would we call it?

The naming brainstorm is sometimes where things go sideways. I mentioned my contempt for acronyms. Event titles can be much worse, especially when religion is involved. We loaded up the whiteboard with an array of cheesy titles. "Beer and the Bible" … "Thirsty Theology" … "Flights and Faith" … "Crafts with Christ." This is where alliteration and good Christian intention miss the mark.

During a pause, Joseph blurted out: "Let's just call it 'Barvangelism.'"

Once again, I thought he was joking. But Brooks liked it. Jake said the name might be interesting enough to pique people's curiosity. To me, "Barvangelism" sounded like we were about to storm the taproom armed with ringlets of *WWJD* bracelets to hurl at the bar patrons. Joseph overcorrected that assumption by suggesting we open the taps and provide free drinks for everyone. I had to remind him that we weren't throwing a corporate junket for the executives at Google or Nike. Jake cautioned that a sloppy room of drunk people might not exactly honor the spirit of the Great Commission from Matthew, chapter 28.

I suggested we go visit the brewery if we were serious about this silly idea. We arranged a second meeting to give us a taste of the space… and a few of the latest Cotch Hop flavors. They were delicious. The first beer I ever tasted, at the age of seventeen, was poured from a two-day-old keg of Natural Light. It was a rough way to enter the world of adult beverages, but I quickly discovered an appreciation for imaginative combinations of barley, yeast, and hops. Ironically, the last time God was part of my palate was probably around the same time. It took a little longer for me to reacquire that taste.

The tasting went well and a date was set. Fun as it was to create, I didn't plan on attending Barvangelism. It overlapped with Rose's swim lessons. Plus, I was skeptical that anyone would show up. Joseph was exasperated by my refusal to cancel plans. How could I not want to be part of, in his words, *the greatest idea a church ever had*? I had to admire his unapologetic exaggeration.

To be fair, this was Joseph's opportunity for validation; a chance to spearhead something new. He had originally joined Turning Point as a pastoral intern while finishing his degree. Now that it was complete, he was hungry to charge forward in leadership. Jake was discerning whether or not Joseph was ready to pastor his own church, maybe even a new site location for Turning Point. In some ways, Barvangelism was one test to show that the young pastor could prove his mettle. A very strange test indeed.

The event was calendared for a Thursday evening, a week or so after the school year opened. Joseph invited a quirky ex-pastor named Ron to be his debate partner for the inaugural event. I met Ron only briefly at the office. He was lanky, but not tall, with a dark complexion. I couldn't place his ethnic roots, although he certainly wasn't from Caucasia. He also didn't look old enough to be an *ex-pastor*. Although, knowing Joseph, Ron's ordination could've been granted by the Church of the Flying Spaghetti Monster.

Joseph claimed the pairing of he and Ron would make for a lively debate. I didn't doubt that was true; pastors are a strange bunch. But what would they talk about? I happened upon the answer sitting next to the paper cutter at the Turning Point office: *CONTRADICTION – Is the BIBLE full of it?*

Now I was really glad I wasn't going.

You might have thought, as I did, that everyone on our staff would be putting full effort behind Barvangelism. Not true. Other than help from Angela and Flake, and me to a much smaller extent, Joseph was mostly on his own. I noticed this tended to happen often. Entire events could be planned and executed without parts of the staff knowing they existed. If that sounds odd, just remember we're talking about more than a thousand congregants. Things happened to them every week. They got sick. They got married. They got depressed. They got curious. They got ideas.

People in a church need a lot of care. Like my friend Darrel says, "It's much more a hospital than a sanctuary." Helping people takes time. It takes strategy and structure. Not everyone on staff was going to be "in the know" all the time. That may not be such a bad thing.

Jockeying for idea promotion seems to be a pretty pervasive issue in churches. It's evident in a church handout with seventeen announcements. How does one choose between the upcoming canned food drive, bake sale, yoga night, singles soiree, mission trip, softball signup, tree planting, potluck dinner, or pole dancing class? You think I'm making that last one up? I'll Google "Pole Dancing for Jesus" right now if you want.

Barvangelism got the green light, but it was not going to get front and center attention. In the end, Joseph had to own it. He had to get people to show up. And he had to make sure it was compelling, fun, and relevant. I'm sure the execution weighed on him. Maturity, spiritual gifts, and work product were being appraised. Joseph camouflaged well. He had an inexhaustible smile and an endearing, almost annoying optimism. If he was nervous or anxious, I never knew it.

In the week leading up to the event, it looked like Joseph was going to pull it off. The Facebook event page listed over 200 people as either "interested" or "going." Flake told me he had no issues setting up the screen, and that the space looked great. In my most thirty-six-year-old dad voice, I asked him if it was "on fleek." He gave me a look that said, "Sometimes I wish you wouldn't say whatever thing that just pops into your head."

I still thought the name left something to be desired. And the topic seemed dreadfully heavy. That said, I now wished I could go. But I had promised Layla an evening away with her friends while I covered swim lessons. I did ask her, just once, about maybe finding coverage for Rose, or somehow switching the girls' night so I could go to Barvangelism.

"Did you just say 'Bar-vangelism?' Dear God, what the hell have you done to my church?"

"So, I guess that's a 'no?'"

"I'm just going to assume that was rhetorical," she said.

I wasn't going to argue with a pregnant woman—especially one with a "surprise" baby. Layla was heading into the second trimester and was prone to saying, "You did this to me!" whenever she got frustrated. Not sure Barvangelism was worth the fight when I was just trying to keep all the living things in our house from destroying one another.

On Wednesday afternoon, the day before the event, Joseph called me in a panic. He told me that Ron had been stung by a bee and was hospitalized. I asked if it was a killer bee. I wanted to know because if not, this seemed like the most extravagant excuse to get out of a public forum debate. He said he didn't know, but that he needed to find a replacement for Ron and was out of options.

I guess Erin was out of town, and Jake had other commitments. No other staff wanted to do it, and the congregants he asked didn't feel comfortable handling the subject matter. So… Joseph asked me if I would take up the mantle. I said, "Ouch. I think I've just been stung by a bee."

"Come on man!" said Joseph.

"Nope, not this time. I've made promises to Layla. Need to sit this one out bud," I said.

"Well, damn. No problem. I get it."

That should've been the end of it. But, because maybe God likes having a bit of fun with me, I got a phone call from Layla five minutes later. She said she wasn't feeling up to going out and that if I wanted to go to that "stupid Barvangelism thing," I could. She'd cleared the way for me to enjoy a night out at a brewery. The catch was… I'd have to talk to a group of people about contradictions in the bible. The alternative was shuffling Rose to the indoor pool with a very real chance of having to change a poopy swim diaper. I decided cleaning diarrhea off my toddler was the more appealing option.

Joseph had learned a trick or two from Jake. He texted Layla directly to see if she'd let me help him out. We had gotten to know Joseph fairly well, and this wasn't completely out of the ordinary. Still, I told him to quit trying to hit on my pregnant wife. Joseph seemed willing to pull out all the stops to get me on board. I've never had a man beg me so hard for anything. Hmm, that sounds a little erotic. Let me rephrase… No one has ever pleaded with me so desperately. I'm not sure that's much better.

I repeatedly asked, "Why me?"

Joseph responded by telling me about a conversation we had a few months earlier. I had mentioned that, for many years, I thought the entire Bible was one big contradiction. This intrigued him. Now that Ron was out of the picture, he thought a more organic conversation with a non-pastor would be even better. He wanted me to act like I had never come to Turning Point, and that I was still this inquisitive agnostic with problems with the bible and organized religion. He also said we could give the crowd a little "Joe-on-Joe action." I believe that was the way he put it.

"First off," I said, "that's gross. Don't ever say that again. Second, I mean, that doubter in me still exists, but I have a different outlook now. I don't think I can pretend to be who I was five or six years ago. It would be disingenuous—basically, everything I used to say the church was. I can't do that, man."

Joseph countered. "You're overthinking it, bud. Just be yourself. It's a 'both-and' type of deal. I'm just saying don't be afraid to lean into those questions you've had. I know they're still rattling around in your head. You've told me before."

"But what about citing scripture? I'm not a seminary scholar. I don't want to sound like a bumbling idiot up there."

"Ha, well, there's no guarantee of that. Look, I've heard you speak to groups before. You'll be great!"

"Yeah, to the staff. Not to 200 people who want to assess your biblical acumen, and then share their opinions about it after two or three drinks."

"Alright, look, I'll give you a few passages to look up tonight, and I'll keep the conversation within that framework. Fair?"

"I swear, this is just your way of getting me to preach a sermon. I still owe you for that crap you pulled on my first day, by the way."

"Well, buddy, here's your chance!"

"Yeah, yeah. Alright. I'll do it. Just don't make it weird."

"Oh, it's gonna be weird. It's *Barvangelism*, brother!"

In hindsight, Joseph might've regretted being so savvy at predicting the future.

# 19

# Barvangelism...
# part 2

I investigated the content Joseph gave me, as much as one man could in a single sleepless night. I looked into the descriptions of temptation in James and Genesis; the resurrection accounts in Matthew, Mark, Luke, and John; and the judgment in Psalms versus Revelations. I read explanations from lots of other people who are smarter than me or at least seemed to know the Bible a lot better. One scholar likened biblical accounts to a court trial. Witnesses may have all seen and heard the same thing, but present varied accounts of events. The testimonies are different but complementary and, in the end, lead to the truth. Not sure if I'd win over any atheists with that argument. And I don't know if that fully assuaged my own inquisition. Maybe Joseph was right—I could easily play the part he was asking me to play.

The next day, I regretted staying up all night. I left the office a few hours early with the intention of grabbing a quick nap and then reviewing my source material in preparation for the evening ahead. I accomplished neither of those tasks. Instead, I answered emails, arbitrarily searched the internet, stared at the Bible, and day dreamed of illnesses that would be believable enough to cancel my attendance. I pulled myself together around 5 p.m., stuffed some dinner into my belly, and hopped into my car. I entered "Cotch Hops" into my GPS, which I do regardless of how many times I've been to a location. Then I slowly backed out of the driveway, hoping a car might zip around the cul de sac and slam into me.

I arrived an hour before showtime; the co-headliner of Barvangelism. The parking lot was expansive, wrapping three sides of the two-story building. Cotch Hops was contained within an unusually symmetrical steel rectangle, painted a deep slate gray. There was a razor-thin strip of green space abutting the north end of the building, flanking the glass vestibule. All else was metal and concrete. I strode across the lot toward the massive white letters painted into the façade, prominently displaying the brewery's name.

I recognized a few of the vehicles along the way. Some of the staff had heard about the last-minute change and came out to show support. It was humbling and reinforced once again that I liked working with these people. Yet I wasn't naïve. Some of them came out to see if I would give them a nice train wreck to talk about with their friends.

I helped Flake and Joseph unload speakers, screens and, for some reason, several bags of peanuts. The event space took up the entire second floor. It was utilitarian, furnished with only the metal stools and aged wood tables that were necessary to host a crowd. The main attraction was the 40-foot long steel bar behind which I could glimpse the tops of the kilns. Max capacity looked to be easily in the low-hundreds.

We were supposed to get started at 7:00. By 6:45, maybe thirty people had trickled into the cavernous room. I was beginning to feel less nervous. Joseph, however, paced mercilessly and couldn't stop bouncing off the early guests like an over-energized pinball. I made him sit down with me for five minutes and order a dark chocolate stout from the bartender to calm his nerves.

By 7:05, there were about 175 people. I couldn't believe it. Barvangelism. Wow. I guess Brooks was right. Maybe it was just odd enough that people had to know—like the time when Brian Fetzer invited me to his *Tour de Franzia* fundraiser. Yes, it was exactly what it sounds like: bicycles and boxed wine.

Joseph grabbed a microphone and provided a prayer followed by an introduction. Then he gave instructions for the ice-breaker. I had no idea this was part of the program. I listened as Joseph instructed the room full of grown adults to pick up the Styrofoam cups filled with peanuts. Then he had Flake change the projector screen to display five questions. "Now," he said, "for every question that you answer, try to toss a peanut into the steel bucket at your table. Let's see who can get the most. Readyyy… go!"

People seem to obey any command spoken into a microphone. I bet we can attribute certain wars in the 20th century to the microphone. But, I'll admit, I had fun assessing the faces of the late arrivers. A few of them took cautious steps backwards as if trying to make their escape. But once you've committed to Barvangelism, there's no going back.

The peanut game subsided, and it was time for the main course. I was sweating profusely. Fortunately, I had worn a black shirt in anticipation of my body's reaction to the nerves. Joseph signaled me to come to the front, next to the projector. I took a seat on the stool opposite his. He laid out the instructions and ground rules. Then he launched into the first topical question of the evening. "Does God really tempt people?"

Almost in unison, heads dropped to their phones. The screen next to me displayed the question, a text number, and large font selections: "YES," "NO," and "UNSURE." I watched the bar graphs advance in the different categories as people submitted their answers. After about a minute, the tallies had finished. The room was split almost evenly into thirds based on the answers. I guess we did have something to talk about now.

Joseph then gave some quick background for James 1 and Genesis 22. He said he didn't want to focus on the singular verses, which are often used in spiritual debates, but rather a rounding of the entire account. I insisted he be the first to answer and allow me to follow his lead.

To no surprise, his response was, "No, God does not tempt people. But he does test us." He went on to explain some of the history, including the use of the word "tempt" in the New King James version versus the word "test" or "prove" appearing in other translations. He finished by reiterating that if one takes the time to soak in the entire Abraham story in Genesis, one can rationally conclude that this was indeed a test and not a temptation. Thus, the two scriptures are not at odds.

"So, what do you think, Joe #2?" he said with a wry smile.

I blanked. I had been crafting my response the entire time he was talking. But when it came time, I just blanked. Have you ever sat in silence for a full twenty seconds? Sounds like a short amount of time, doesn't it? Well, let me tell you—it is not. That day, I learned just how long a second feels. It feels like an eternity. Joseph finally leaned over and whispered, "Hey man, you okay?"

I shook out of my brain glaze abruptly, almost whacking him in the head with my elbow as I raised the microphone. "Honestly, Joseph, I don't know what the hell you're talking about."

The crowd erupted. Sadly, it wasn't because I intentionally said something droll or witty. It was more because it had been some time since the audience had watched a fish try to crawl across dry land. Why was I up here in the first place? I looked down at my mostly full dark lager sitting on the floor. I reached for the glass and pulled a healthy swig. The brew took just enough edge off for me to regain my thoughts.

I recovered—or at least I think I did. I asked Joseph a rapid-fire series of questions: "How in the world is someone supposed to know which translation to read? Or which account to believe? And who does one trust to help unlock these secrets for us?" I spoke for a few more short minutes about the confusion of inconsistent messaging across Christianity. I tried to wrap up by noting that, yes, in some of its literal translations, the

Bible appears to contradict itself. Only through conversations with smart and open-minded people of faith had I come to understand that there might be some contextual learnings that I am… well… still learning about.

My reflections weren't as polished as Joseph's. Heads in the crowd displayed just enough intentional eye contact mixed with a few slight head nods to let me know they were engaged. I didn't feel I'd ever recover from my initial gaffe. I just drank more beer to wash it away.

We moved through the other questions in much the same way. The dialogue started to hum along. I was finding some semblance of rhythm with Joseph. He's a comedian pastor—you know the type. So, it wasn't hard for him to keep the crowd smiling. Well, most of them.

We'd been at it for about twenty minutes and were ahead of schedule. Joseph and I were midway through our conversation about the different resurrection accounts in the four canonical gospels. He was arguing that it would be more difficult to believe the resurrection occurred if all the accounts were identical. It would assume everyone had copied a single author, and we'd be left to rely completely on the veracity of that one person's witness.

I could tell Joseph was close to finishing his resurrection talking points when an older gentleman stood up unexpectedly. The man had a thick head of white hair and was seated about ten feet from us. I noticed that he faltered a bit under the weight of his own body. I couldn't tell if this was due to age or inebriation or both.

Catching Joseph mid-sentence, the man's slurred words and pitched voice removed all doubt. This guy was drunk. Or, at the very least, on some heavy painkillers. "Tell me, Pastor, what gives YOU the autorithy to ssspeak about such things?"

Joseph's face retreated into a look of surprise; his mouth slightly agape from not being able to finish his sentence. "Uh, can I help you, sir?"

"Yeah. You can start by telling all the people here what a liar you are!"

"Come on, man, let's not do this right now."

"Ha. You're the one doing this little event. Can't take the heat? Get… get out of the… get out of the…kitchen!"

"Okay then. Well, this is probably a good time for a break, everybody. Feel free to grab a drink or use the restroom, and we'll finish the conversation when you get back. Let's say… ten minutes."

"I'm not done with you!" the elderly man shouted.

He picked up the bucket of peanuts from his table and hurled it at us. I would surmise that this crazy fellow was very good at bar games—the kind where your skill increases after a few drinks—because he nailed Joseph right in the face. The bucket made a loud clanging noise, and peanuts exploded out of it like an overheated bag of popcorn.

Until that point, Joseph had been superb in his handling of the situation. Stay calm, be polite, defuse the conflict. Unfortunately, peanuts must be his kryptonite. Joseph grabbed the man by the shoulder and began dragging him toward the exit. I should mention, Joseph is built like a Division III college linebacker. Not big enough to be Division I, but stocky enough to put a hurtin' on someone. I could tell he had quite the death grip on the man's skinny bicep. While being escorted, the man continued his rant. "There is no God! There is no God! Owwww! You're hurting me! Save yourselves!"

A few of the other attendees came over to help. They had seen Joseph's skin change from pink to green, clothing beginning to rip. The rest of the room stood in silence and watched. Joseph and the others then disappeared down the stairs with the old man. The room slowly rose up in a collective whisper. Some people left. Others headed to the bar. A few cleaned up the peanut mess. I suppose we all have different ways of processing these things.

About fifteen or twenty minutes later, Joseph returned. He apologized to the crowd, then offered up an ill-timed prayer. We tried to resume the debate and finish out the final five minutes of our conversation, but the attendees no longer had questions about the reliability of the Bible. They just wanted to know what happened to the man who had been lugged out of the building by the hulking young pastor.

We precipitously concluded the presentation portion of the evening and moved quickly into the talking and drinking. I was surprised at how many folks stuck around. Despite the odd interruption, people were engaged in real dialogue, much of it relating to the religious topics with only the occasional peanut joke. I suppose there aren't many opportunities afforded to talk about spiritual opinions in a non-church setting. Although I did overhear a woman come over to Joseph and say, "Pastor, is that the first time you've had peanuts thrown at your face?"

For my part, I had proven the extent of my "pastoral" abilities. And I didn't need to hear any false compliments, so I decided to make my escape after thirty minutes or so. A pregnant wife, by the way, provided a wonderful excuse to leave early for just about anything. I thanked the brewery bartenders on my way out. As I opened the door, a brisk early autumn wind hummed across my cheeks. Nearing the parking lot, I turned and saw him. The peanut man was staggering to my right, in a flanking position. He seemed to be heading toward his car.

My feet pivoted, and I began closing the gap, walking toward him. My brain kept telling my body to autocorrect, but my limbs didn't respond. What was I doing?! By the time I gained control again, it was too late. I was standing right next to the man. He momentarily awakened from his stupor. Our eyes locked, and he took a moment to register. "You! What do *you* want?"

I told the man I was sorry for what happened and asked if he needed a ride home. He shirked my offering, fumbling with his keys instead. We were standing next to a late 1990s model Honda Accord. The paint on the hood was almost entirely peeled back to the windshield. He leaned against it for balance. I kept talking, though I'm not sure what I said or where the words were coming from. I calmed him down enough to pick up bits and pieces of coherent dialogue.

The street light lit up two shadows that startled me for a moment. They were congregants from Turning Point. One was Claire, whom I'd met before. The other was a young guy wearing skinny jeans. He introduced himself as Curtis. The man leaning on his tired Honda finally gave up his name as well. It was Jim. That was good. I didn't want to have to say, "Listen, Peanut Man, you shouldn't be driving."

Though it was hard to make out what Jim was saying, we discerned that he lived nearby. The longer we talked, the more his mood softened. His tone was no longer combative. He wasn't offensive or derisive. Quite the opposite. Jim just looked sad. I mean, in part, he was just plain drunk, but he also displayed an intoxicating amount of pain.

I have no idea why Jim confessed. Maybe because he had a small audience. Maybe because he'd had too much to drink. Or maybe because he had been holding it all in for too long. Whatever the case, Jim started to open up to us. He told us about losing his wife to heart failure. He told us about losing his job. He told us about his fractured network of family and friends that had dwindled to nothing. The words came dripping out. Granted, it became difficult to sift reality from the babbling thoughts lost to the bottle and imagination. What was authentic was that Jim was a man in serious misery.

At one point, he began sulking in fits and starts. I watched in amazement as Claire pulled him into her broad shoulders. I checked my phone for the time. We'd been talking to Jim for almost an hour. I needed to get home. As I was thinking this, I heard someone starting to pray. Then I felt a hand on each of *my* shoulders.

For a moment, I stepped out of my own body and was

watching myself, as if I was a ghost. My first thought was: *What's up with those pants, Joe?* Layla was right; I desperately needed a new wardrobe. My second thought was: *Why am I praying?*

I rubbed my eyes to clear up the scene I was watching. It was too odd to be real. An inebriated old man, a hipster with a lip ring, and a tall transgendered woman were all leaning against a dirty, old Honda Accord listening to a ridiculous church worker pray over them in a parking lot.

I can't tell you a single word of that prayer, because I don't remember it. I just remember the moment. When I was done, Claire led Jim to her car. Curtis took the keys to the beat-up Honda and, after a few turns of the ignition, got it to fire up. Then they both pulled out of the lot. I never saw Jim again.

During the last two months, I've pondered that brewery parking lot. It was the first time in my entire life that I had done anything like that. It was abnormal, off-putting. It was instinctive. And probably the most "Christian" thing I've ever done.

Turning Point hosted another Barvangelism event last week. I wasn't able to go, but I heard the flinging of bar food was absent from the event this time. What an offbeat church this was. Or maybe all churches are unusual if they're actually trying to practice what they preach. Maybe Jake's words were beginning to resonate with me now more than they ever had. *If it results in positive transformation for just one person who can no longer deal with the burdens of a life gone sideways, then it's all worth it.*

I could easily have been Jim just a few years ago. Maybe

I still am him in some ways. I did throw a bowl of popcorn at Layla and Rose last week—although our skirmish ended in a tickle fight instead of a group prayer in the driveway. Yeah, we're pretty cute these days. And I try not to take those moments for granted. I will often flounder as a father and as a husband—that's a certainty. But these last two years have taught me just how much I love my family. More than that, I've learned how to better care for people I don't even know.

And that brings me to you. I'm sure you didn't love the idea of me working for a church. I killed a career that, up until then, perhaps you had been quietly proud of—by your measure of success. You called me for the first time in a while recently, and you asked me why I took the church job, and what it was like. I never got the chance to tell you. So, I've spent several hours in this stark room, unloading everything I can remember from the past two years, talking until I'm tired of my own voice, and watching you fade away.

I used to resent our relationship. I'd even poke fun of it at times. We've both let each other down in monumental ways. I suppose these last two days have been my buoyant attempt at reconciliation. I'm not certain you've heard a word I've said. But I have to believe I've gotten through somehow. I hope so because we're coming to the end of our time. I just talked to the doctor. She said there's nothing more they can do. Unless there's some kind of medical miracle, you are about to die.

# 20

# Reconciliation

My cynical side says you made your bed, so you have to lie in it. Right now, you're experiencing that proverb quite literally. There are choices you made which, in part, probably contributed to the stroke that led to the coma that put us where we are now. And there are other decisions that created rifts in your relationships. Over time, those rifts created holes, which turned into massive chasms. Entire years, even decades, were lost. Throughout this conversation, I've realized just how much you don't know about my life as it is now.

There's a lot we could talk about from our past. We could talk about the messy divorce when I was nine. We could talk about the strict values you tried to pass onto me that sometimes made me feel trapped. We could talk about you putting on a suit on Sunday and then taking your pants off on Monday to sleep with the woman you met at Buffalo Wild Wings. We could talk about how you left me to play the role of both brother and father when Rick struggled through his teen years. Or just the general way you've been absent from our adult lives.

Instead, let's talk about Zion. Do you remember driving for three days in that beat-up van all the way to Utah? We slept in some funky hotel room near Amarillo. We stopped at a Native American reserve to buy arrowheads. We drove an hour out of the way to watch the sun set over the Grand Canyon. We got lost, so we just slept in the van under a big oak tree. You and Rick kept farting the whole night, refusing to crack the windows.

When we arrived at the park, we hiked down to the bottom of a colorful canyon, which looked like it was illustrated by Dr. Seuss. We ate peanut butter sandwiches while skipping rocks on the creek. You rescued Rick when you caught him trying to pee on a scorpion. Then we pitched a small tent and slept together under the cool desert stars. It was, and still is, one of the most magical trips I've ever taken.

And there are other good memories. You taught me how to throw a nasty curveball. You took Rick and me to our first theme park, where we rode our first roller coaster. You brought us to the Hershey factory and quoted Willy Wonka while we glided through the river of chocolate. You taught us about kissing girls. Well, that might be a bad example. At any rate, you were a lead character in the early years of our biographies.

It's a shame that our paths diverged so severely later in life. Sure, you'd pop in now and again to check on us. And there were times when you lent support. But we were never as close as we were when I was a kid. You got caught up in what I assume was some kind of mid-life crisis. Mom married Bruce. And we all got on with our lives. Maybe time simply moved faster than we thought it would.

Wait a sec—I just remembered something. You didn't meet your mistress at Buffalo Wild Wings. You met her at Applebee's. Jeez, Dad! I'm not sure which is worse. Did she offer you the two-for-twenty deal? Never mind. I'm glad you can't answer that.

Anyhow, I know you were raised to be Christian. I've seen the twenty-seven framed pictures of Jesus at Grandma's house. But somehow that deep-seated, old-time religion didn't help you with compassion and commitment. Not that you don't know what those things are. They're just not part of your natural repertoire. They don't seem to be ingrained in your DNA. I get that now. And, in a lot of ways, it has helped me overcorrect with Layla and Rose. I often try to go out of my way to let them know how much I love them. I'm guessing you wish you would've set aside more time for *your* family.

And when I mentioned my faith journey starting with Layla and Rose, that wasn't exactly true. It really started with you and Mom. You did your best to expose Rick and me to the world of Christianity. It just didn't take. The church you introduced us to was not one that accepted us for who we were. We were too young to know how to fake it. We weren't as shrewd as you or as skilled in the art of deception. And, unfortunately, we earned a few scars in the process. However, having gone through it, my religious lenses are broader. I feel, in some ways, as if I've been tested. And I'll tell you, for a long time, I was certain that churches would soon be a thing of the past—decaying buildings once inhabited by naïve gatherings of people.

But many have been predicting the demise of the church for years. I think now it might be more relevant than ever. I hesitate to say this because it'll sound a bit trite, but Turning Point might be the reason I'm sitting in this room. Otherwise, I probably would have gone on pretending you didn't exist. Or, maybe I would've stopped by to pay respects for a few minutes. I wouldn't have spent two days trying to get you to hear me over the continuous clicking of hospital equipment. I only wish I'd done this sooner. A two-way chat would've been nice.

Still, I hope it has been fun listening to your son describe his absurd adventures working for God. You used to be pretty funny when I was a kid. I figured you might get a kick out of carnivorous goats, Mexican turtlenecks, and the oddest description of the Bible anyone has ever attempted. And I know for a fact that you used to love watching the "Top 10" list on David Letterman. I had to provide you with the church version. Seriously, how 'bout those church marquees? Unbelievable.

Dad, I'm not sure where this vocation will lead. Maybe I'll burn out in a year or two. Maybe Pastor Jake will have a meltdown. Or maybe it'll become my life's work. It's probably too soon to tell. I just know I'll be living life a bit differently, no matter what. And, to that end, I believe I owe you a few more answers.

Have I finally found the meaning of life? Uh, no. Not even close. But perhaps that's a silly question to ask anyway. A better one might be: Have I found meaning *in* my life? To that, I'd have to say *yes*.

Did I really discover God? I'm not sure. I've glimpsed him at work more now than I ever have. I still haven't reconciled all the questions surrounding faith and science, other than to conclude that perhaps they don't have to be mutually exclusive. Both require some level of faith when you get to a certain point. But I can't deny that my purpose is different now. I've lived a lot of years aspiring to get as much out of the world as I could, all the while worrying what it thought of me. That's not going away any time soon, but it's nice to sense a greater purpose. Something more fulfilling.

And then there are the Christians. How did I phrase it? Are they as nutty as a porta potty at a peanut festival? The answer to that is 1,000 percent, without a doubt, no arguments, refunds, or exchanges… YES.

Let's start with me. I think it's fair to say that I am now a card-carrying Christian. And not simply because I was raised that way. I just prayed for a drunken man. Out loud. In the parking lot of a brewery. Next to a woman who had just completed sexual reassignment surgery. And I was strangely okay with all of it.

I also told you about Bridget Bergstrom. She's in every church. She just goes by a different name. Consequently, the two of you should've hooked up at some point. I think it could've been truly special. Somehow, I feel like she would have kept you in line. You might not have been so quick to adulterate if you came home and Bridget was standing in the foyer. She'd be holding a big rusty pair of scissors and a string sack filled with two tennis balls. The moment that sack was sheared off, you'd have gotten the point really quick.

And yes, beyond the congregants, there's the shootout among religious sects and systems. Often it feels like the Bible is everyone's gun, and they just load in different brands of bullets. Life or death situations are created when perhaps a friendly arm-wrestling match would've sufficed. But everybody just keeps firing and reloading. The ballistics team can't even get in there to analyze the forensics as internal, external, or terminal. I suppose the lead investigator finally throws up his hands and says, "Well, screw it. I guess just keep shooting each other until you're all dead."

Some folks would have a picnic with that entire analogy. I'm sure you'd be one of them.

Maybe Christians are typically like most any other large faction of people. They can make an astonishing impact through their aggregate talents and resources. And they can take on a herd mentality, which often ends in the trampling of those who stumble and fall.

So, does the church really have the moral high ground? I think we've proven that it doesn't. And I certainly don't. I'm often terrible about being receptive to other people's ideas about family, faith, life, death, politics, sex, and so on. I guess Jake, Erin, and Joseph try to steer me to look at these issues using scripture as a guide. And sometimes, their "guidance" is simply the best interpretation that a pastor can surmise, even after years of study. Sometimes their advice sounds correct. Sometimes it feels a little off.

Either way, I assume the best result is more people loving their neighbors and accepting the grace of a benevolent creator—even if they suck at this a lot of the time. So yeah, Christians are crazy. But I still love 'em. And if I'm going to figure out this life and faith thing, I'm going to need them. I can't do it alone.

Where does all this leave you and me, you ask? I'm not sure. At least you're not alone right now. I heard what happened with your girlfriend. She skipped town with all the money right after your stroke. And Rick still won't visit. You've left quite the shit storm in your wake, Dad.

Here's the thing. Remember when I asked you what kind of funeral you wanted to have? That's going to happen soon, so you better start thinking about it. So far, I'm not too optimistic. You've neglected a lot of friends and family as you've aged into your twilight years. I'm not even sure that's the proper idiom. Sixty-six seems far too young to be talking about your funeral.

But I'm going to do us both a solid. I'm not going to talk about all the ways you let me down. I'm just going to recount the two days we spent in this hospital together. I'll tell them we laughed and cried. I'll tell them we caught up on life and rehashed adventures. I'll tell them we spoke about God at length. I'll tell Rose about our conversation. And, at some point, I'll tell Nolan... your new grandson. He'll be here in a few months. I'll tell them stories are important, even those that are messy or incomplete.

That's the difference church has made in my life. Three years ago, you were an afterthought. I wasn't even mad really. I was complacently indignant. I honestly didn't care what happened to you. And if you were to have passed away three years ago, I doubt I would have spoken at your funeral. If I did, it wouldn't have been kind. Now, I'm ready to talk. No, you're not that great a person. But neither am I. And there was at least a season where a less-than-perfect father-son relationship scored some wins. And, I forgive you.

Speaking of the funeral, there will undoubtedly be a few non-Christians at a funeral like yours. They're the ones who will roll their eyes when your sister says, "He's in a better place. I'll see him again when I get to heaven."

"I apologize for my aunt Bonnie," I'll say. "The woman is a tad crazy. She collects ornamental birdfeeders."

She does, by the way. You know it's true.

At some point, I'll probably throw out an invitation to church, because that's what I do now, I guess. I tell people about my imperfections. I tell them about my hypocrisy. And I tell them that, when left to my own devices, I have failed to deal with those things very well. I'll probably get funny looks. But church workers are used to that. Because churches are full of funny people. The kind that, sometimes inadvertently, help you find meaning in life.

As per the Christians in the room, God help me when your cousins from Alabama crash into town like a wrecking ball. I'm going to need some lessons in tongue holding before they get here. And I might need to check out some self-help books afterward. Speaking of that, didn't two of them try to collaborate on a book? What was it, "101 Ways to Be a Better

Christian?" If I remember correctly, they tried to incorporate the movie *101 Dalmatians* into it. Every chapter was named after one of the puppies or something. And the devil was sometimes described as Cruella de Vil. With family like that, it's no wonder you're so messed up.

Although, to be fair to the Christian-dalmatian book project, pastors do get asked all the time to provide the silver bullet for better Christian living. It's usually addressed with edicts such as "read the Bible more," or "go to church more," or "radically change everything in your life to fully accept the unyielding love of your savior Jesus Christ… more." The last Christian bookstore I visited had shelves and shelves of self-help books—most with borderline-creepy pastoral selfies adorning the dust jacket covers.

With your cousins in town, it's possible the topic could come up at your funeral. I'd like to avoid it like the plague. However, I think I might have an answer if someone ever asks me how to be a better person of faith. First, I'd probably say, "Don't be like me." Self-deprecation is an easy default mode. But if I could get past that, I'd tell them: 1. Talk to a stranger; 2. Forgive someone; 3. Pray for someone. All good Christian anecdotes come in threes. Everyone knows that.

In truth, those are all things you forced me to confront. You've become a stranger to me. How much do we know about each other from the last fifteen years? You're also someone who thinks and acts a lot differently than I would. And that has presented us with some conflict or, at the very least, resentment.

Seeking a resolution, I've had to forgive you. Because I

have fallibilities just like you. I used to think yours were worse than mine, which just made it easier to avoid my own short-comings. Not that it lets you off the hook completely. Some of that stuff you did was just damn awful. But holding onto it was like letting a virus eat away at me while the antidote was just across the room.

And yes, I'm going to pray for you before I leave here. Is it odd that if I open with "Father," I could be talking to you or God? Don't let that go to your head. That is, unless it might stir something that helps you wake up. You never know. I feel like you're the kind of person to have everyone think you're dead only to pop out of the casket with your middle finger raised to say, "Y'all can't get rid of me!"

Maybe I'll go ahead and offer up a prayer now. It should be fitting for the situation.

Let's bow our heads. *Lord, maybe you can send your hand down one more time, to stop these motherfuckin' bullets.*

Like I said, I still have a long way to go.

Wait. Are you smiling?

# Acknowledgments

If you're reading this, I hope it means you enjoyed The Church Worker so much that you simply had to know who else was involved in the project. If you were offended by this book, don't blame any of the people I'm about to name. They mostly thought I was crazy for doing this in the first place.

First, thank you Megan for: A. Loving us all amidst the perils of parenting two precocious children in a dual-working household with Chihuahua-Beagles (or "Cheagles") nipping at our knees and B. Giving me the freedom to be me, idiosyncrasies and all. To Jordana Berliner, you probably will never know how amazingly helpful you were in driving me to continue writing while you poured out edits and advice from afar. To my brothers from other mothers – Matthew Washburn, Phil Lee, Eddie Rockensock, Aaron Likas, and Martin Leathers – I appreciate you listening to my attempts at becoming an audiobook narrator. Yes, I too am tired of hearing me talk. And thanks mom and dad for giving birth to me, hopefully through a labor that wasn't 34 hours long.

Countless others tossed me an assist and made me realize how lucky I am to be rich in friendship. Y'all are amazing people. And of course, thanks to anyone who took the time to read this book. It was meant to make you laugh and feel less burdened by your imperfections. Finally, thanks be to God.

Made in the USA
Middletown, DE
17 February 2021

33940733R00144